THE MOTOR APPARATUS
OF THE
MAMMARY GLAND

THE MOTOR APPARATUS
OF THE
MAMMARY GLAND

M. G. ZAKS
Sechenov Institute of Evolutionary Physiology

Translated by
D. G. FRY, B.A.

Edited by
A. T. COWIE, D.SC., M.R.C.S., PH.D.
National Institute for Research in Dairying
Shinfield, Reading

CHARLES C THOMAS · PUBLISHER
Springfield · *Illinois* · *U.S.A.*

CHARLES C THOMAS, PUBLISHER, 301-327 EAST LAWRENCE AVENUE
SPRINGFIELD, ILLINOIS

Translated from M. G. Zaks: FIZIOLOGIYA DVIGATEL'NOGO APPARATA MOLOCHNOI ZHELEZY SEL'SKOKHOZYAISTVENNYKH ZHIVOTNYKH *published by* Izdatel'stvo Akademii Nauk SSSR Moscow/Leningrad 1958

FIRST ENGLISH EDITION BY OLIVER & BOYD 1962

Translation © 1961, Oliver and Boyd Ltd

Printed in Great Britain by The Sidney Press Ltd, Bedford

CONTENTS

	Foreword to the English Edition	vii
	Foreword	ix
I	The Storage Function of the Mammary Gland	1
II	The Physiology of Milk Ejection	27
III	Features of the Production of Milk Fat and other Milk Constituents	111
IV	The Relationships between Milk Removal and Synthesis	141
V	Some Features of Mammary Gland Function and of Milking Practice	153
	Supplement: Elastometric Studies of the Motor Function of the Mammary Gland in Woman	174
	References	178
	Subject Index	189

FOREWORD TO THE ENGLISH EDITION

Owing to the great progress that has been made in lactational physiology, a great many facts have been accumulated. This justifies devoting a whole book to the detailed examination of selected aspects of lactational physiology. This book is such an attempt to deal with one most important question, that of the motor function of the mammary glands.

I shall be extremely happy if my book is of some use to our British colleagues, in whose debt we have all been since the Russian translation of Folley's excellent monograph.

The basic Russian text has not been greatly revised. I have merely added a review of some of the more important Soviet papers published since the book appeared. Another new feature is the Supplement, which is devoted to our findings concerning the physiology of the mammary gland in the woman. I attach great importance to the further development of these studies. Quite apart from their practical importance, the problems of human lactational physiology are profoundly interesting in relation to comparative physiology. A broad approach, based on comparative physiology and on evolutionary concepts, is, moreover, an important condition for progress in lactational physiology.

M. G. ZAKS,

March 1961. Leningrad, U.S.S.R.

FOREWORD

Problems of the physiology of lactation have been intensively studied during the past decade in a number of laboratories both in the Soviet Union and abroad. The extensive factual material thus accumulated is now in need of critical reviewing.

Various aspects of the lactation process have been studied, but the study has been uneven. Considerable attention has been paid, for example, to aspects of the development of the mammary gland and to the biochemistry of lactation; at the same time we have fallen far behind in our study of the most important side of the question—the very nature of the secretory process in the mammary gland. In my opinion, one cause of this backwardness is to be found in the serious methodological obstacles due to the very structure of the mammary gland. The extensive storage system of the alveoli, ducts and cisterns in which the milk accumulates is in itself an unusual dead space. Milk extracted from the teat for study can only give an extremely provisional picture of the secretory events taking place in the gland at any given moment. We are, of course, continually seeking ways of overcoming this obstacle. It is for this reason that a detailed knowledge of the processes of milk accumulation and removal, i.e., everything that underlies the function of the motor apparatus in the mammary gland, becomes of extreme fundamental importance.

It is the aim of the present work to give an account of the basic information at our disposal on the motor function of the mammary gland. This branch of lactational physiology has been studied in the greatest detail, especially in the Soviet Union, and a great deal of factual material that requires consideration has been accumulated.

I fully realize, of course, that the motor and secretory functions of the mammary gland are intimately connected and that their separation is purely a convention. A detailed study of the motor function of the mammary gland can be treated as an essential preparation for fundamental studies of the secretory process, which still remains the most important task of lactational physiology.

I have attempted in this book to summarize matters relating to the accumulation and removal of milk in all mammals for whom this aspect has been studied. Most space has, however, been given to data concerning farm animals and especially cows. This is both because the latter were and remain the main subject for the experimental investigation of lactational physiology and because a detailed knowledge of the various aspects of the lactational function in the cow is of great practical significance. It is my hope that, in addition to appealing to specialist physiologists, this study may also be of some use to practical workers (specialists in animal husbandry and veterinary surgeons) in solving their most important problem—that of markedly increasing the productivity of dairy cattle.

CHAPTER ONE

THE STORAGE FUNCTION OF THE MAMMARY GLAND

Storage system of the mammary gland. It is a typical feature of the mammary gland that its secretion—the milk—is continuously produced, but that the gland is freed of the accumulated secretion periodically. Certain other glands, such as the liver and kidneys, have a similar property, but it is only in the mammary gland that the receptacle in which the secretion is accumulated is in such close anatomical connexion with its secretory elements. This circumstance makes it possible for the secretion already produced to exert a diversity of influences on the further course of the secretory process.

The second specific feature of the mammary gland is the actual method of its evacuation. In other glands of external secretion the discharge of the secretion from the aperture of the discharge duct is brought about solely as a result of the action of expulsive forces developed by the secretory or motor elements of the gland itself. Evacuation of the mammary gland requires an additional external force that is exerted in practically all mammals by the young in the act of suckling, and in dairy animals (cows, goats, sheep, horses, camels, etc.) in hand or machine milking as well. The need for this additional force is occasioned by the fact that the outlet ducts of the mammary gland are equipped with sphincters, decline in the tone of which at the moment of milk removal is not sufficient to enable the internal expulsive forces to overcome it. The primitive mammary glands of the *Monotremata* (the platypus and the spiny anteater) that have no nipples are an exception. Here the milk flows more or less freely and the young do not suck but lick it from the hairs or the surface of the skin. It is true that the young of these animals clearly stimulate the reflex removal of milk and to some extent express it from the ducts on to the gland area by pushing with the "bill".

The marsupials, the young of which are very poorly developed, are a similar exception. The young animal is still not able to suckle and the milk is not sucked out, but is injected into its oral cavity when the mammary gland is compressed by a special subcutaneous muscle. Some aquatic mammals (e.g., whales) evacuate the gland by a similar mechanism, owing to the specific conditions attached to feeding the young when submerged.

The mammary gland is able to accumulate considerable amounts of secretion owing to the existence in it of a complex system of cavities and ducts—the storage system of the gland. There are considerable differences in the structure of the storage system in different types of mammal, and it is most complex and developed in dairy animals, especially in the cow. The cavities of the alveoli make up a considerable part of the total udder capacity. The diameter of individual alveoli varies between 0·1 and 0·4 mm. (Bogdashev and Eliseev, 1951), but these data are highly provisional. If one takes into consideration that the form and dimensions of the alveoli are subject to great variation, calculation of their total capacity becomes complicated. It will be shown below that when the udder of high-yielding cows is quite full not more than 40% of a single milking is contained in the alveoli and, in part, in the ducts of fine calibre.

The initial finest milk ducts begin from the alveoli; they merge to form milk canals, the diameter of which is increased by junction. Merging of the canals gives rise to larger collectors—milk passages that discharge into a cistern—the gland's general reservoir—separately for each quarter of the udder. The cistern of the gland leads into the cistern of the teat and together they form a general cavity that is sometimes divided by a more or less well-developed circular fold at the level of the base of the teat. It is only rarely that this fold is so developed as to separate completely the cavities of the upper and lower sections of the cistern. In a milking cow this anomaly is a defect that requires surgical treatment. The cistern of the teat leads into the teat canal, which has an outlet at the lower end of the teat.

There are no reliable data in the literature on the potential capacity of the various ducts in the storage system of the udder; it is clear that when the udder is fairly full approximately 60% of a single milking in high-yielding cows is contained in the cisterns and milk passages.

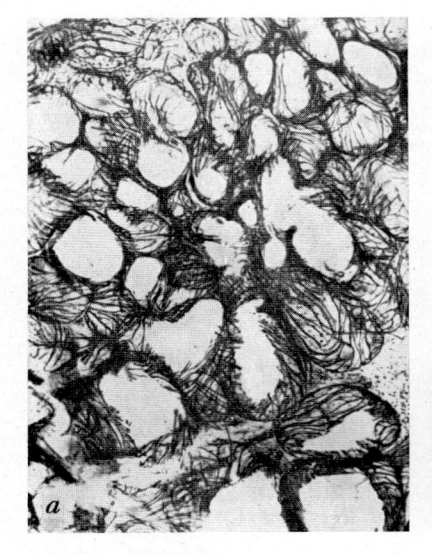

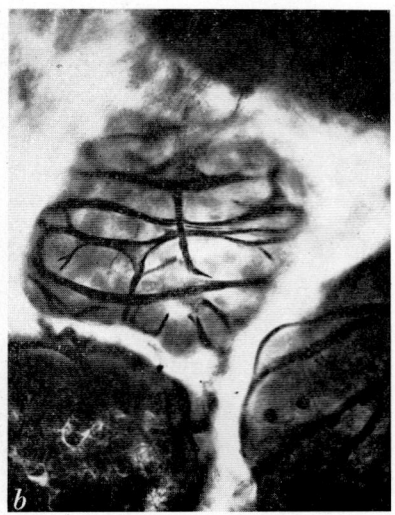

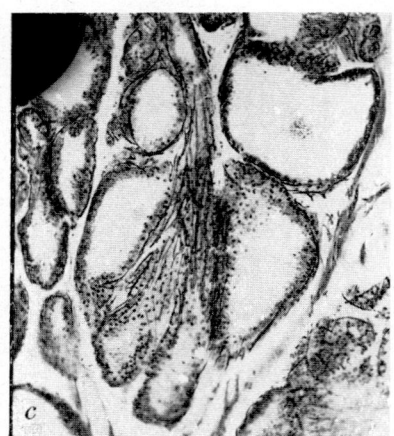

FIG. 1. The myoepithelial structure of the mammary gland.
(From Richardson, 1949.)
(Photographs by courtesy of Mr. K. C. Richardson.)

a—myoepithelial network of alveoli fixed when extended.

b—a single myoepithelial cell with branching processes on a small alveolus.

c—myoepithelial elements longitudinally disposed in the wall of a duct.

The walls of all the sections of the storage system contain contractile elements that comprise the complex motor apparatus of the gland. In the walls of the alveoli and the finest calibre ducts these are the myoepithelial cells, which form a distinctive network round the alveoli or lie along the major axis of the ducts (Fig. 1). In addition to the myoepithelium, the walls of the finest calibre ducts contain longitudinal fibres of smooth muscle to which circular muscles are added in the larger ducts. The smooth musculature is most developed in the walls of the cistern, especially in the teat region. A thick circular layer of smooth musculature—the teat sphincter—is situated in the walls of the teat canal.

This, in its most general form, is the structure of the storage system in a cow's udder. The principle is the same in other dairy animals and the only differences are in details.

The main structural elements of the motor apparatus of the mammary gland have been described by a number of authors from von Langer, Langerhans and Heidenhain to Rikhter (1939), Espe (1950), Bogdashev and Eliseev (1951, 1957). The existence of two types of contractile element in the gland—myoepithelium and smooth muscles—and their functional significance is generally recognized by the majority of authors. Only particular isolated details of the function of these elements remain unclarified and in dispute.

Thus, Richardson (1949) thinks that the myoepithelium alone plays the major part in the evacuation of the mammary gland and that the smooth musculature does not in general have any importance in this respect. In his opinion the development of the smooth musculature both in the fine calibre ducts and even in the large ducts and cisterns is so insignificant and its distribution so random that it cannot have any particular significance for the evacuation of the mammary gland. It has, however, to be stated that adequate factual proof of this opinion is not provided in Richardson's work.

Some mammals have no cisterns and the milk passages communicate directly with the surface of the nipple. In these cases the capacity of the gland is increased by special dilatations of the milk passages—the milk sinuses. Mammary glands constructed on this principle include those of man, the dog and the pig.

The relationship between the processes of milk accumulation and removal. Secretion is continuous in the lactating mammary gland of a cow. All the milk produced in the intervals between milkings is accumulated in the internal receptacles of the udder, where it remains until the gland is evacuated by milking or suckling. In the lactating cow this evacuation takes place 2–3 times or at most 4–5 times in 24 hr. It is natural that quite considerable quantities of milk, up to 10–12 litres and more, accumulate in the udder storage system of high-yielding cows. Consequently, the storage system of the udder is adapted to contain variable volumes of milk. This presupposes the presence of special mechanisms which, on the one hand, make it possible for the storage capacity of the udder to be fully utilized without interfering with the secretory process and, on the other hand, allow the milk to be removed rapidly and energetically at the required moment. It is this latter process that is known as "milk ejection".

Milk ejection is an intricate complex of active reactions of the motor apparatus of the udder that develop in a reflex manner under the influence of milking or suckling stimuli and which ensure that the udder is rapidly evacuated.

Milk ejection is a definite link in the lactation process that connects the complex system of neuro-humoral coordinations with other processes taking place in the mammary gland and in other systems of the organism, the function of which is in some way connected with lactation.

The secretory activity of the cells of the mammary gland, the filling of its cavities with milk, complex variations in the volume of the secretion and pressure fluctuations at the moment of milk ejection, in brief everything that is taking place in the mammary gland at any point in its activity, can be a source of afferent impulses which are of fundamental importance for the reflex autoregulation of all aspects of the lactation process and which are also responsible for the interconnexion and interconditioning of this process and the functions of the organism as a whole.

When analysing the physiological mechanisms of secretion, milk accumulation and ejection, one should bear in mind that they are the result of reflex acts that are intimately connected and that are separate links in the process of lactation.

The process by which the storage system of the udder is filled in the intervals between milking is of particular interest from this point of view. The efficacy of milk ejection will depend in large measure on the extent to which the udder has been filled before milking, how the milk is distributed in the different sections of the storage system, on the initial pressure existing in the udder cavities and on other factors. In other words, the nature of udder filling determines the background for the functioning of the contractile elements of the alveoli, ducts and cisterns at the moment of milk ejection.

The ability of a dairy cow to accumulate considerable quantities of milk in the udder cavities between milkings, i.e., the capacity of the udder, is one of the important indices of the cow's productivity. Therefore, the capacity of the udder and methods for its determination have been repeatedly studied by veterinary workers, anatomists and physiologists. There are great variations by breed, lactation number, stage of lactation and especially milk productivity in the absolute dimensions of udder capacity in the cow. This explains the great divergences in the data obtained by different authors when studying this question. A not insignificant factor is the absence of a single criterion for the very concept of "udder capacity", and especially the absence of a standard method for its determination. In this connexion, it should be emphasized that one of the least successful methods is *post-mortem* determination of udder capacity from the amount of liquid which can be introduced into its cavities. This might not be worth mentioning but for the fact that this method has been used in recent work. Thus, Swett and Matthews (1953) give data for the udder capacity of Holstein-Friesian cattle (27 animals) obtained by filling the udder of the dead animals with a solution of formalin.

In the judging of dairy cows, particular attention is usually paid to estimating the collapse of the udder after milking completely dry and also to other indices (fineness and stretch of the udder skin, the presence of skin folds (reserve) etc.) that provide direct or indirect information on the ability of the udder to alter its dimensions in relation to the degree of filling. Considerable importance is also attached to the histological structure of the udder (Liskun, 1912; Nemilov, 1915, 1924, 1927; Al'tman, 1945; Mosimann, 1949; and Arzumanyan, 1952). In addition to the numerical ratios of the parenchymatous cells and the stroma, account is also taken of dimensions, i.e., the capacity of the alveoli and ducts. Davydov and co-workers (1939) proposed a system of external measurements of the udder that would give an objective estimate of udder collapse.*

The suggestion by Azimov and Lapiner (1939, 1940) that udder capacity should be determined from a maximum single milking was very fruitful. This figure can be easily established for a given cow by analysing the farm records of single milkings or experimentally by artificially extending the normal interval between milkings by a few hours.

Beguchev (1950) proposed that the level to which the udder was filled when the interval between milkings was significantly extended should be taken as an index of maximum capacity. Under these conditions the secretion of milk is greatly impaired, if not totally halted. This is shown by variations in the chloride content and acidity of the milk, by the upsetting of the normal ratios between the protein fractions and, finally by the reversed absorption of lactose into the blood and its appearance in the urine, which latter factor is taken by the author as an index of the moment when maximum capacity has already been reached. This method for determining the capacity of the udder clearly makes it possible to describe variations in this index in comparable terms in relation to the lactation number of the animals, their productivity, lactation periods and other factors. It is clear, however, that capacity as determined in this way can hardly be treated as physiologically regulated capacity. We are here concerned with the forced, excessive stretching of the walls of the storage system to the anatomically possible limits. This stretching is naturally accompanied by a rise in pressure within the udder to values that are not compatible with the normal secretory process. The author, however, clearly has this in mind when, like Azimov, he stresses the importance of the period of "free milk formation", when milk secretion proceeds without the interference of ever-increasing pressure.

Turner (1955a) uses another approach to determine maximum udder capacity. He considerably extends the interval between milkings and graphs the relationship between the volume of the milking and the duration of the interval from data for a number of successive determinations of a single milking on different days with different intervals between milkings. He takes the peak in the curve, after

---

* These morphological indices may possibly play some part in an evaluation of the capacity of the udder, but their practical importance is very limited.

which there is a sharp decline in milk formation, as an indication of the moment when udder capacity is reached. There are a number of features in common between Turner's results and Beguchev's data, as is quite obvious from a comparison of the curves in Fig. 2. One can assume that Turner's critical remarks on Beguchev's work (more accurately, in relation to his use of the moment when lactose appears in the urine as a criterion of udder fullness) are due to the fact that Turner was clearly only able to become acquainted with this paper through a brief abstract and not from the original.

Further analysis of the problem of udder capacity should be directed to a study of the physiological features by which the animal is enabled to accumulate a considerable quantity of milk in the storage system of the udder without increasing the pressure within the udder above the level at which it will begin to interfere with secretion.

It has already been indicated that the walls of the storage system include, in addition to elastic tissues, contractile elements—smooth musculature in the cistern and ducts and myoepithelial cells in the alveoli and fine-calibre ducts. When the storage system is filled with

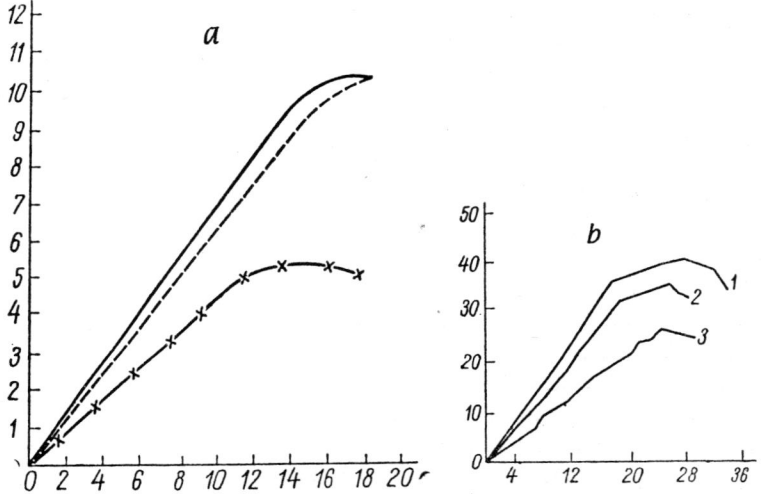

FIG. 2. Intensity of milk synthesis in relation to the time interval after milking.

a—the process of milk synthesis in various cows (from Beguchev, 1950); *b*—the process of milk synthesis in one cow at the beginning (1), in the middle (2), and at the end (3) of the lactation (from Turner, 1955a). *X-axis*—time after milking (hr.); *y-axis*—amount of milk (*a*—in kg.; *b*—in lb.).

milk the tone of these contractile elements should be and is lowered. A similar phenomenon takes place, as is well known, in other organs, the volume of which alters sharply in relation to the volume of their contents (pressure changes in the cavity of the organ being insignificant); e.g., in the stomach, the gall bladder and urinary bladder. The regulation of the tone of the musculature in these organs has now been quite fully studied. It has been established that both an increase and a decrease in tone is reflexly effected, mainly as a result of the stimulation of receptors in the walls of these organs. It is impossible to reduce the process by which the udder is filled with milk to a simple elastic stretching of the walls of its storage system. The capacity of the udder to store greater or lesser amounts of milk is due not only to the anatomical dimensions of its receptacles, as Espe assumes (1946) without foundation, but also to the complicated physiological mechanism that regulates the tone of the udder's motor elements. This is the property to which we shall refer as the capacity function of the udder, thus extending the existing concept of udder capacity. This terminological distinction is of fundamental importance. It emphasizes that full account should be taken when studying the capacity of the udder of the unity of the anatomical structure and physiological function of its storage system.

The dynamics of udder filling. Correct understanding of the storage function of the udder depends first and foremost on a knowledge of the dynamics of its filling. Immediately after quite efficient milking the udder is not totally evacuated, but always contains a certain amount of milk known as residual milk. This residual milk is an important question to which we shall often have to return. Here we shall only note that milk formed in the period following milking is distributed through a storage system that has not been entirely evacuated and is mixed there with the residual milk. Thus, not all the milk to be obtained at the next milking is formed in the period after the preceding milking; a smaller part of it was synthesized earlier. It is evident that total "renewal" of the milk in the storage system takes a long time. At any rate, when small amounts of coloured fat are injected into the cistern (Espe, 1946) it is gradually removed in the course of many milkings and traces are to be detected in the milk even 10 days after introduction.

It should also be remembered that the composition of the milk can undergo further changes after its formation and transfer into the cavity of the gland's storage system. This is shown, for example, by Azimov's data (1955). He and his colleagues established that there is a continuous and very energetic exchange between the blood and the milk. When they injected ^{32}P-labelled phosphate into the cistern of one teat they found that the radioactive phosphorus appeared very rapidly both in the blood and in the milk of the other quarters. The vigour of this exchange is also indicated by the fact that when a known amount of ^{32}P was injected into the cistern of a goat only half of the injected isotope was milked out in the ensuing 24 hr. Within 10 minutes of injection up to 0·5% of the amount of ^{32}P injected had passed into the blood. The process of milking considerably increases the rate at which the phosphate passes from the storage system into the blood. Further studies will reveal how other components of the milk behave in this respect; the mechanism of the phenomenon is moreover not clear: is it simple diffusion, or are more complex physiological processes involved?

Later studies by Azimov and his colleagues (1961) revealed that ^{45}Ca and sulphur ^{35}S, as S-labelled methionine, injected into the cistern are subjected to similar reabsorption (the authors' own term). Since the sulphur enters the blood as inorganic compounds, relatively "large" molecules are split in the process of reabsorption. It is of interest that sulphur is taken up more energetically by the blood than is $Na_2H^{32}PO_4$. The stimulating effect of milking and massage on reabsorption, which has already been established, is evidently of a reflex type: of the neurotropic agents, phenamine greatly stimulates and sodium amytal inhibits reabsorption. The injection of posterior-pituitary extract intensifies reabsorption, but less than milking. In Azimov's opinion, milk secretion and the partial reabsorption of certain of its components are balanced and interconditioned processes. Thus, adrenocorticotrophin (ACTH), which has been found by Flux, Folley and Rowland (1954) to retard milk secretion, also greatly inhibits the reabsorption of phosphorus.

The whole storage system becomes filled as milk is formed. If one is to clarify the successive steps in the filling of its various sections, one must select definite objective indices. The most important index is the ratio between alveolar and cisternal milk. As was already known, a part of the milk flows freely at the beginning of milking; all that is necessary to remove it is to overcome the resistance of the teat canal sphincter, but to obtain the remaining part of the milking one must induce active milk ejection. There are various opinions on the relationship between these parts of the milking. Thus, for example, Hammond (1936) thought that approximately 40% of the milking was present in the cisterns and ducts of large calibre, while the remaining 60% was situated in the alveoli and the ducts of fine calibre. We shall see below that it is scarcely possible to make such a comparison without taking into consideration the extent to which the udder is filled and that the ratio is highly dynamic.

Zaks and Pavlov (1952) used the following procedure to make a detailed study of the ratios between the cisternal and alveolar milk. Before milking commenced but after normal cleansing of the teats and udder, a catheter, through which all the milk present at that moment in the cistern (and in ducts of large and possibly even of medium calibre) flowed freely, was inserted into one of the teats. The usual milkmaid was then summoned and she milked the remaining teats, that had not had a catheter inserted, after normal preparation. The milk ejection reflex developed and a certain additional quantity of milk, that had been present in the alveoli and ducts of fine calibre before milking, commenced flowing through the catheter. This volume is treated as alveolar milk. It was first established by a special test that under these conditions the evacuation of the unmilked quarters is as effective as is that of the milked quarters. After the flow of the alveolar milk through the catheter had ceased and the catheter had been removed, a further small amount of milk could be obtained after additional massage or other stimulatory manipulations: we have provisionally called this portion the "strippings". A detailed study of the strippings is of fundamental significance in some experiments.

I was the first to suggest at the Second All-Union Conference of Dairy Workers (Zaks, 1951) that the separate portions of a single milking should be distinguished. Shortly after this Cowie *et al.* (1951) put forward terms that were almost the same as mine, except that they proposed "sinus" milk instead of "cisternal" in their article "Terminology for use in lactational physiology". Later Grachev (1953) amended my terminology, replacing "cisternal" by "mechanical, "alveolar" by "reflex" and "stripping milk" by "additional". Ogorodnii (1953) later used his own terminology to describe the same phenomena. It is, of course, permissible to introduce new terms to describe new facts. But we are not concerned with whose terminology should be accepted: whether priority should be given to the authors who first drew attention to a given phenomenon or whether the terminology of later investigators is found more suitable. What is important is that the division of a single milking into separate portions, however they may subsequently be named, is now generally accepted and is absolutely essential in the study of the most diverse aspects of the activity of the mammary gland.

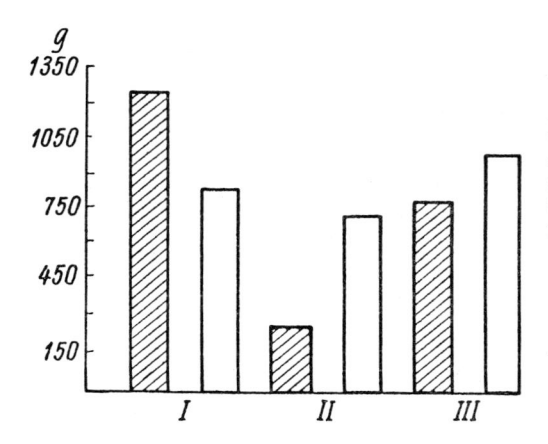

Fig. 3. The size of the cisternal (shaded columns) and alveolar (white columns) portions of the milk (in g) for a single milking at various milkings.

I—5 a.m. milking;
II—1 p.m. milking;
III—8 p.m. milking.

In later studies I was able to show that the ratio of cisternal to alveolar milk in a given cow is not constant, but varies dynamically in relation to the size of a single milking and to a number of other factors. The individual qualities of the animals are here of fundamental importance. In some cows and goats the ratio of cisternal to alveolar milk can be quite different even when the single milkings are identical. We still have no conception of the extent to which these individual differences may be connected with anatomical or functional features in the udder of a given animal.

From 115 measurements on 11 cows yielding on average 8630 g. at the morning milking, 4030 g. at midday and 6170 g. in the evening it was found that the cisternal portion was on average 60% of the morning milking, 26% of the midday and 45% of the evening.

These ratios are shown even more clearly in Fig. 3, where the absolute figures for both portions are presented instead of percentages. It is quite evident that the alveolar portion is more constant than the cisternal portion. One can assume that the portion of the udder's storage system containing the cisternal portion is a reserve store of the udder in which milk only begins to accumulate after the alveolar section is, in the main, full. Considerably larger volumes of milk can accumulate in the cisternal section than in the alveolar. In some experiments we obtained 2500 g. and more of milk from the cisternal section of one quarter of the udder. Thus, Espe's data (1946), according to which the four cisterns contain not more than 1 l. of milk, are unreliable.

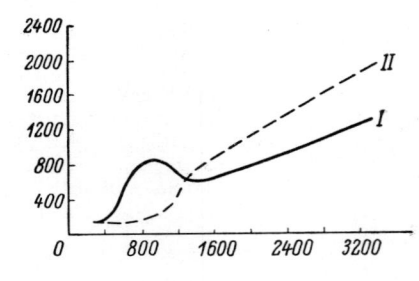

FIG. 4. Variation in the size of the cisternal and alveolar portion of the milk in relation to the level of udder filling explained in text.

Our data were obtained from high-yielding cows, the average milk yield of which in the 1950 lactation was approximately 5200 kg. It is possible that these ratios would be differently expressed in other less productive animals. There can be no doubt, however, that further research in this direction will help to answer a question that is also of practical importance; namely, which section of the storage system is most concerned in yielding increased storage capacity when the milk production of the animal increases?

The suggestion just made that the cistern is of importance as the main reservoir is further confirmed when the measurement data are processed in a slightly different way, as mentioned above. In Graph 4 the values of the total milking (in grammes) from a given quarter of the udder are plotted along the x-axis and the cisternal (II) and alveolar (I) portions of the milk for a given value of the total milking separately along the y-axis. Thus when the

TABLE 1
DYNAMICS OF FILLING OF THE CISTERNAL SECTION

Hour after milking	Name of cow and amount of milk (g.) in cistern						
	Zolotaya	Roza	Neitral'-naya	Bylinka	Shpinatka	Shvedka	Average
1st	0	0	0	0	0	0	0
2nd	0	0	0	0	0	0	0
3rd	20	0	60	20	60	150	52
4th	0	100	250	40	150	100	106
5th	55	150	300	175	100	—	156
6th	200	420	650	690	115	650	454
7th	400	660	—	1435	1070	680	849
8th	500	1845	745	—	1600	—	1172
9th	1260	—	1117	—	1600	1090	1267

storage system is only slightly filled all the milk will be found in its alveolar section, but subsequently when a considerable quantity of milk accumulates the cisternal section will tend to be filled and will become the main reservoir. These data from successive milkings were fully confirmed in another variant of the experiment (Zaks, 1955). In six cows of different productivity the size of the cisternal portion was determined by cannulation of the same quarter of the udder at various times after milking. The results obtained are given in Table 1.

The dynamics of udder filling in the cisternal section are shown even more clearly in Fig. 5, which is a graph constructed from the averaged data of Table 1, in which the natural errors of individual determinations due to the inescapable necessity of making measurements at different hours and not even on the same day are to some extent eliminated. Fig. 5 shows that the cistern is empty in the first and second hours, that relatively small amounts of milk enter it in the third, fourth and fifth hours and that it is only later, between the fifth and eighth hours, that the cistern is filled rapidly. It is only after the ninth hour that the rate of cistern filling declines somewhat.

Almost identical ratios were found by Tverskoi and Dyusembin (1955) in goats: in these animals, as in cows, hardly any milk enters the cistern in the first hours after milking but an energetic influx begins in the fourth hour after the preceding milking. The graphic representation of the process of milk transference to the cistern (Fig. 6) given by these authors is very reminiscent of my own Fig. 4. Note that, even after influx commences, milk continues to accumulate in the alveolar section, but that after a certain point the amount of milk entering the cistern exceeds that secreted by the gland in the given period. The authors concluded that under certain conditions there may be a reverse flow of milk in goats from the cisternal to the alveolar section.

If one rejects the clearly unfounded hypothesis that there is a low level of milk secretion in the first four hours after milking, it becomes quite certain that milk does not enter the cisternal section during this time, since it is retained for various reasons in the "upper storey" of the udder, in the alveolar section of the storage system. It is only after the latter is full that the transition begins and milk flows into the cisternal section. This flow is clearly not continuous and even but rhythmic. This was first noted in goats as long ago as 1917 by Voskresenskii. Later, G. N. Pavlov (see Bogdashev and Eliseev, 1951) observed, when experimenting with goats in which both teats were cannulated for a prolonged period and the milk flow was graphically recorded, that there was an asynchronous fluctuating increase in the discharge of milk in both halves of the udder.* All this points to the existence of a

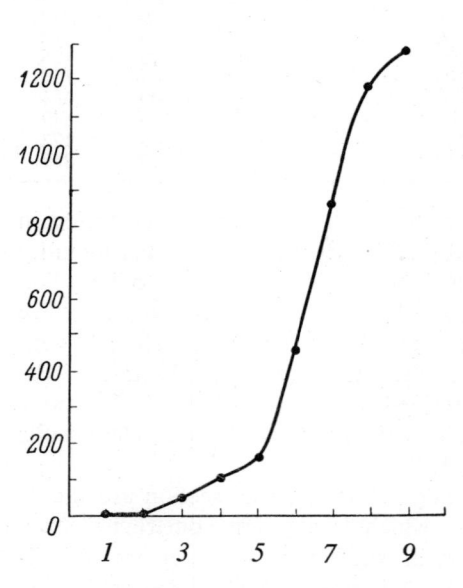

FIG. 5. Passage of milk into the cistern in the interval between milkings.

X-axis—hours after milking; y-axis—cisternal volume of milk (ml.).

* It is still not clear how this process takes place in cows. I encountered unexpected procedural difficulties when trying to study this in experiments involving prolonged continuous cannulation of the teat and there was marked inhibition of the flow of milk into the cistern.

mechanism which first makes it possible for considerable quantities of milk to accumulate in the alveolar section and prevents this milk from passing over to the cistern until a definite point has been reached, and secondly regulates this transition from that point onwards. One must remember above all that milk in the

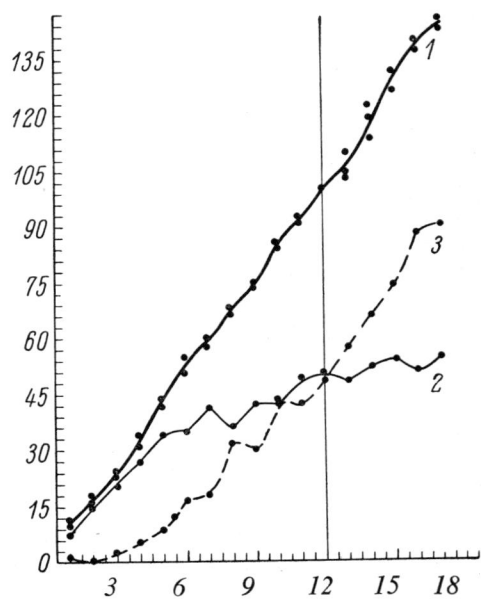

FIG. 6. Dynamics of the filling of the storage system of a goat's udder with milk. (From Tverskoi and Dyusembin, 1955.)

1—total milking; *2*—alveolar milk; *3*—cisternal milk. The line parallel to the y-axis marks the end of the 12-hr. period. *X-axis*—hours after previous milking; *y-axis*—quantity of milk (as a percentage of the milking for 12 hr.).

alveolar section is contained in an extremely complex system consisting of many hundreds of thousands of alveolar cavities and fine ducts of capillary diameters. Quite large quantities of milk can be retained in the branched network of these stores for purely physical reasons (capillarity, cohesive forces, etc.) in the same way as a liquid that soaks through a sponge is retained. One can, however, only speak in a conventional way of the purely physical properties of this living "sponge", since it is clear that in the process of its "saturation" there must be complex rearrangements of the tone of the contractile elements in the walls of the alveoli and ducts.

The significance of these purely physical factors in the distribution of milk in the storage system of the mammary gland should be taken into consideration even if only because they run counter to the force of gravity, the importance of which to the distribution of milk in the udder and in particular to the transfer of milk to the cistern was formerly overstressed. Purely out of curiosity we recall Zietzschmann's opinions (1923), to the effect that after formation the milk descended by gravity into the cistern and then gradually filled the storage system "from the bottom upwards". This view would be quite acceptable for a liquid poured into an empty bottle, but is scarcely applicable to the storage system of the udder.

We now have every reason for stating that the system of ducts incorporates mechanisms by which the alveolar section is separated from the cisternal section and the transfer of milk to the latter is actively regulated. Data concerning the existence of constrictions, interceptions and dilatations, especially at the junctions of ducts, have been given in a number of earlier studies (Rikhter, 1939) and an attempt has been made to link these with the mechanism by which milk is retained in the ducts.

I would also cite a work by Bogdashev and Eliseev (1951), in which there are direct indications that thickenings of a circular layer of muscle fibres "simulating sphincters" exist at the mouths of milk canals.

The existence of similar sphincters in the lactating mammary gland of a mouse has been established by Zotikova (1955) and Levitskaya (1955) (Fig. 7.) When the gland was examined under the microscope they observed typical annular constrictions on small and medium ducts a little above their junction with the main duct. Similar constrictions develop when adrenaline in a concentration of 1×10^{-5} is applied to the surface of the lobule of the gland being studied, and when the peripheral end of one of the nerves entering the parenchyma of the gland is stimulated. Zotikova observed that after the nerve had been stimulated for 15 minutes, the section of the duct proximal to the constriction was considerably extended and filled with secretion and that the

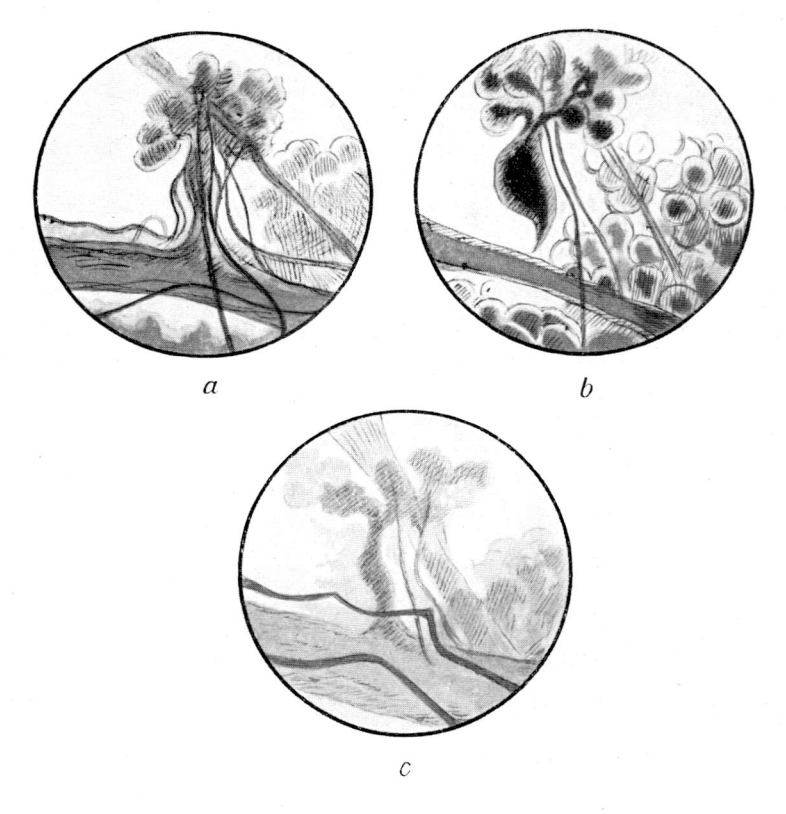

FIG. 7. Mammary gland of a mouse. Complex of alveoli with a duct entering the main duct. (From Levitskaya, 1955.)

a—initial state; *b*—effect of adrenaline; *c*—effect of posterior-pituitary extract.

sphincter was clearly an insurmountable obstacle to the passage of the secretion. After stimulation was discontinued the diameter of the duct was equalized throughout its length and the secretion passed into the distal section of the duct. One may consider that the passage of milk from the alveolar section to the cisternal section is either facilitated or impeded by the tone level and tension of such sphincters. It stands to reason that milk will enter the cistern when the tone of the sphincters is weakened whilst the tone of other contractile elements of the alveoli and the ducts is enhanced.

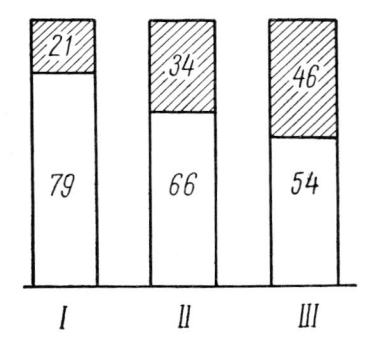

FIG. 8. The effect of denervation of the right half of a goat's mammary gland on the amount of the cisternal (white section of column) and the alveolar (shaded section of column) portions of the milk (%). (From Tsakhaev, 1953.)

I—before operation;
II—1 month after denervation;
III—during the subsequent lactation.

Whittlestone (1950) thinks that a function analogous to that of the sphincters may be fulfilled in the ducts of fine calibre by the myoepithelial cells described by Richardson (1949) that lie along the length of the ducts and give rise to valve-like folds that impede the discharge of milk (Fig. 1c).

The tone of the contractile elements of the alveolar section is clearly reflexly regulated. Tsakhaev (1953) has shown that after one half of a goat's udder is denervated there is a considerable increase in the capacity of the alveolar section, which it is difficult to explain other than by a lowering in the tone of its contractile elements due to a decline in nervous control (Fig. 8). Tsakhaev's findings are fully confirmed by Astrakhanskaya (1955), who discovered that after denervation of one half of a goat's udder there were changes in the size of the alveolar and cisternal portions of the milk identical to those described by Tsakhaev. When Astrakhanskaya made a histological study of the denervated glands of goats and guinea pigs she discovered considerable expansion in the small and medium ducts, which it is difficult to associate with anything other than interrupted regulation of the tone of their smooth musculature. She also found that there was an irreversible contraction in the cavities of the alveoli by comparison with the alveoli of normal control glands (Fig. 9).

Val'dman (1958) has obtained proof that in goats the tone of the storage system is dependent on efferent innervation. Unilateral transection of all the sensory roots from L_1 to L_5 gave rise to the same variations in function as did total denervation: decline in the milk ejection reflex on stimulation of the deafferentated side, increase in its sensitivity to posterior-pituitary extract, etc., but the typical increase in alveolar volume after total denervation established by Tsakhaev and Astrakhanskaya was not observed in these experiments.

The following outline can be suggested for the passage of milk from the alveolar section into the cistern, based on the concept that the tone of the mammary gland's storage system is reflexly regulated. At a certain stage in the filling of the alveolar section pressure within it rises to a level at which it begins to stimulate receptors in the walls of the ducts. When this happens the tone of the sphincters is reflexly lowered at the same time as the general tone of the contractile elements of the storage system lying "above them" is enhanced. This causes a certain part of the milk to be discharged into the cistern, immediately after which pressure in that section of the storage system that lies above the sphincters is reduced, the intensity of this milk discharge reflex is weakened and the initial tone pattern is restored until new milk accumulates. This process is illustrated diagrammatically in Fig. 10.

It is evident that this reflex does not develop throughout the udder at one time. This is shown by the data already cited on asynchronous ejection in the separate halves of the udder (in goats). We do not exclude the possibility that even within one lobe of the udder this reflex may develop in a series of stages in the separate parts and not simultaneously.

Olenov (1954) concluded from considerations that will be given in detail at a later point (p. 127) that one part of the secreto-motor complexes of the udder secretes milk that is more fatty than that secreted by the other parts. Owing to the high inertia of their motor apparatus little of the products of these complexes are

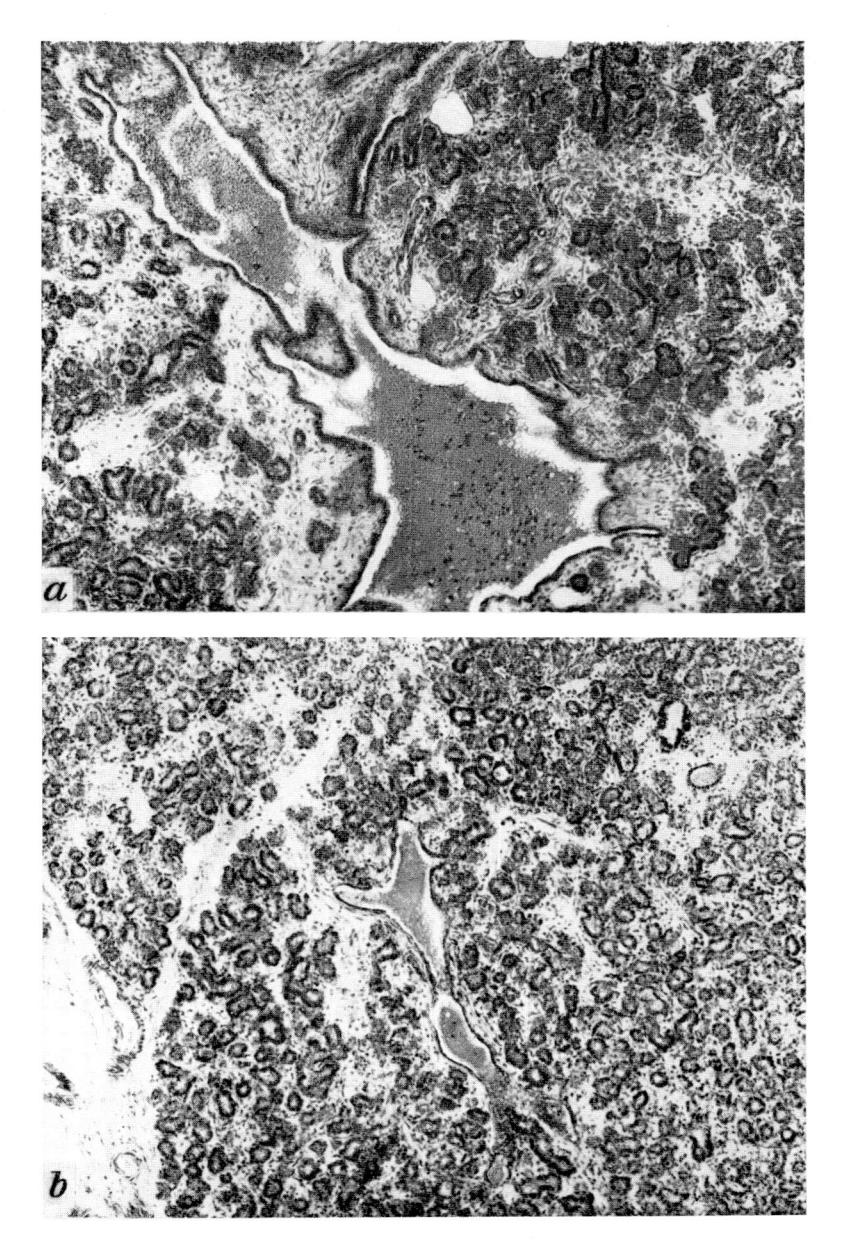

Fig. 9. The effect of denervation on the tone of the mammary ducts in a guinea-pig. Specimen taken at the end of pregnancy, 14 weeks after denervation of a sexually immature animal. Stain haematoxylin-eosin. (From Astrakhanskaya, 1955.)

a—right denervated half of the gland;

b—left normal half of the gland.

evacuated into the cistern in the intervals between milkings but are evacuated most intensively during milking or suckling under the influence of exteroceptive stimuli.

It should not be thought that the discharge—the passage of milk into the cisterns—is due exclusively to interoceptive (baroceptive) stimuli originating from the storage system of the gland. This movement can equally be due to exteroceptive stimulations

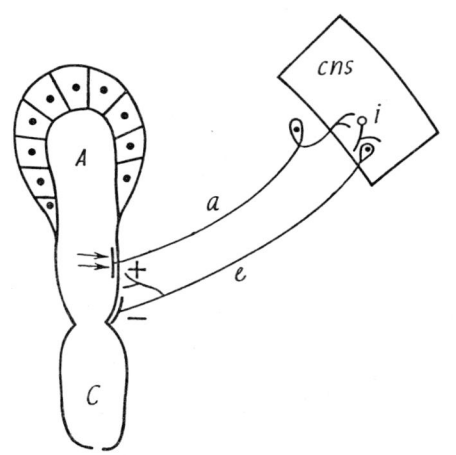

FIG. 10. Diagram of reflex regulation of the passage of milk into the cistern.

A—alveolar section of the storage system; *C*—cisternal section of the storage system; *cns*—central nervous system; *a*—afferent neuron; *i*—internuncial neuron; *e*—efferent neuron. The arrows show the excitation that develops when pressure is increased; the plus and minus signs indicate contraction and slackening of the corresponding motor apparatus of the storage system.

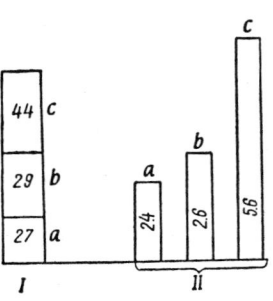

FIG. 11. Amount of the cisternal (*a*), duct (*b*) and alveolar (*c*) portions of the milk and their fat content. Averaged data (%). (From Borsuk and Zaks, 1955.)

I—total milking for one quarter of the udder taken as 100%; *II*—fat in the separate portions.

from the skin of the teats and the udder. Borsuk and Zaks (1955) have shown that under certain conditions it can easily develop in the course of milking, as can be seen from the following experiment. A cannula was introduced into one cistern before milking commenced and before the arrival of the customary milkmaid, and there was none of the usual preparation for milking (washing and drying of the udder, massage and other manipulations). All the milk in the cistern naturally flowed through the cannula. Light massage and washing of the udder immediately after the cistern had been totally evacuated in this manner caused the flow of milk to recommence. The total amount is usually equal to the volume of the cistern and is sometimes even greater. The out-flow is energetic and in a stream and has the appearance of normal milk ejection associated with contraction of the alveoli. In composition (fat content), however, this milk is much closer to cisternal than to alveolar milk (Fig. 11). If we now milk the other teats, milk is once again discharged from the cannula and its fat content corresponds to the alveolar portion; this is milk ejection in the normal sense of the term. Even our first experiments showed that this phenomenon (discharge) develops in some cows under the influence of stimuli that are clearly of a conditioned reflex type (approach of the milkmaid, the sound of her voice, the clatter of the milk pail, tying the tail, etc.).

In her later detailed experiments Borsuk (1955b) showed that a conditioned discharge reflex can easily be produced to such stimuli as the sounding of a given note, feeding, etc. In this form the phenomenon of discharge cannot be observed at all stages in the filling of the storage system. When, for example, the period after the preceding milking is considerably extended and a large part of the milk is already in the cistern, one cannot normally observe discharge. It develops most easily when the cistern is only slightly or moderately full, i.e., when the cistern is also being filled most intensively under normal conditions. It is clear that under these experimental conditions the milk that passes into the cistern is the portion that is ready to leave the ducts. Even in the absence of exteroceptive stimuli produced by the experimentalist this transfer would still take place, but in this case it would be effected by interoceptive stimuli from the walls of the ducts. Such discharge undoubtedly has a reflex mechanism and scarcely differs in principle from the mechanism outlined in Fig. 10. The only basic difference is that in this case the stimulus is extero- rather than interoceptive.

We are here dealing with a process that is quite typical, namely with a reaction of the musculature of the ducts that makes it possible for the milk to enter the cistern freely. We shall make a detailed examination of many examples of such reactions below when considering the act of milk ejection itself. Here we shall content ourselves with indicating that this mechanism is of fundamental importance both to the dynamics of udder filling in the intervals between milkings and to the evacuation of the udder during milking.

Intracisternal Pressure in the Intervals between Milkings. The tone of the contractile elements of the udder's storage system as a whole is of great importance in the regulation of intra-mammary pressure in the intervals between milkings. This factor is of great importance to the efficacy of the secretory process, since an increase of pressure within the storage system above a certain level leads first to interruption and finally to total cessation of milk secretion. This is so important that the very concept of "udder capacity" can, in essence, be defined as the ability of the animal to accumulate the largest volume of milk in the storage system of the udder for the smallest rise in pressure. Until quite recently, however, the importance of intramammary pressure as a factor limiting milk secretion was not quite correctly understood. According to Espe (1946): "As the pressure of the accumulating products gradually increases there is a corresponding drop in the rate of milk formation." The ability of the animal to accumulate larger or smaller amounts of milk without interference from increasing pressure is associated with the existence in the udder of certain anatomical spaces forming reserve storage, the using up of which leads to a rise in pressure that is incompatible with the continuation of secretion (Petersen and Rigor, 1932).

According to Krzywanek and Brüggemann (1931), these storage reserves are associated with variations in the tone of the musculature of the storage system, which is lowered as the milk accumulates. These authors consider, however, that in this case the tone is not reflexly regulated but is regulated purely locally: the smooth musculature is weakened by purely mechanical factors (stretching) as milk accumulates in the ducts and cisterns.

A detailed study of pressure changes in the storage system of the udder in the intervals between milkings leads to the conclusion that there are much more complex mechanisms in operation. Beguchev (1950) notes that pressure rise is slow in a period of "free milk synthesis" and that the rise in pressure is not proportional to the amount of milk accumulated. This question has been studied in greater detail by Zaks and Pavlov (1952). The analysis of the results of 115 measurements of intramammary pressure in 11 cows with the cisternal section of the udder at various degrees of fullness has shown that the nature of the variations in this pressure cannot be explained purely physically when related to the volume of the cisternal milk. Fig. 12 shows that when the cisternal section is filled up to 400–500 g., pressure increases more or less in proportion to the degree of filling of the cistern and reaches approximately 16–18 cm. of milk. When, however, the cisternal portion is further increased to 1400–1500 g. from 500, pressure rises very slightly and is clearly not in proportion to the degree of filling of the cistern. The nature of the pressure rise subsequently changes once again when the cisternal volume exceeds 1500 g. and becomes similar to that which obtained in the initial (0–500 g.) sector of the curve.

This type of curve shows that there is a special reflex mechanism actively regulating pressure at the expense of a change in the elastic properties of the walls of the receptacle, i.e., in the tone of their contractile elements.

It is evident that when the cistern is filled with up to 500 g. the accumulating milk extends the elastic elements of its walls passively and the pressure rise is almost linear and subject to purely physical laws. As soon, however, as pressure attains 16–18 cm. of milk it acquires sufficient force to excite the receptors in the walls of the cavity. This gives rise to a reflex that inhibits and lowers the tone of the musculature of the cisternal section. Subsequently, at above

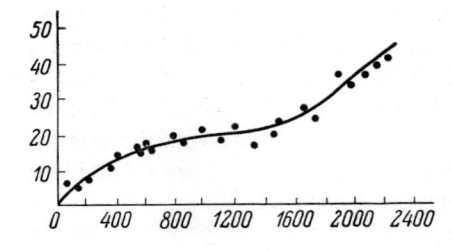

FIG. 12. Dependence of pressure within the teat cistern on the size of the cisternal portion of the milk.

X-axis—cisternal milk (in g.); *y-axis*—pressure (cm. of milk).

1500 g., the possibilities of this physiological mechanism are already exhausted and pressure once again begins to increase as intensively as before: the physical factor has once again come into force. This is clearly the close of the period of free milk synthesis and further rise in pressure will lead gradually to the decline and subsequent complete cessation of milk secretion.

The curve in Fig. 12 has been constructed from averaged data for high-yielding cows (average yield per lactation 5200 kg.), all except one of which had undergone at least 4–5 lactations. This feature is quite different in young, high-yielding animals (Fig. 13). When we compare the data for the cows Zhar-ptitsa, Zolotaya and Bylinka, it is evident that the cow's capacity actively to regulate intracisternal pressure depends on the animal's lactation number and is clearly trained from calving to calving. This circumstance can scarcely be ignored when milking first-calf heifers, especially when selecting the most rational milking frequency for a given cow.

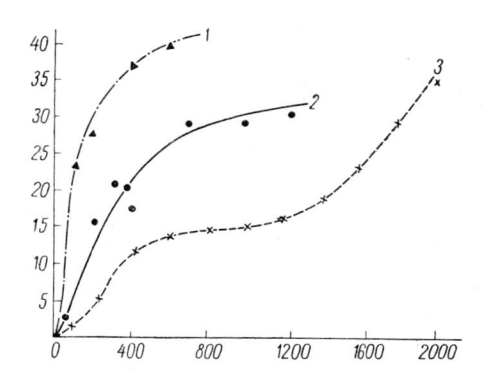

FIG. 13. Intracisternal pressure in cows of various lactation numbers.

1—Zhar-ptitsa (first-calf heifer); *2*—Zolotaya (2 calvings); *3*—Bylinka (6 calvings). Remaining notations as in Fig. 12.

Nikitin and co-authors (1953) fully confirmed our data on variations in intracisternal pressure as set out above and showed that the pressure rise in the cistern in the intervals between milkings is quite insignificant and clearly not in proportion to the degree of filling. They also established that pressure within the cistern can maintain a constant, fairly low level even when the interval between milkings is considerably extended. These authors agree with us in interpreting their facts from the point of view of the concept of reflex, adaptive variations of the tone of the musculature in the walls of the udder.

Summing up what has been said, we can arrive at definite conclusions. The main hypothesis that intramammary pressure above a certain level has a negative effect on milk secretion still holds. This gives rise to an important practical rule: the milking régime for a given cow must be such that intramammary pressure is not allowed to rise to a level where secretion is affected.

Thanks, however, to the existence of physiological mechanisms that prevent excessive pressure rise in the storage system and adapt the tone of the udder spaces to the increasing volume of their contents, the storage system is able to hold considerably larger volumes of milk than could be assumed from purely anatomical proportions. The data presented above show that in highly productive cows the storage function of the udder is trained and develops from lactation to lactation. Another important practical rule follows from this: when milking young and newly-calved cows when their productivity is rising rapidly, the frequency of milking should be such that the as yet undeveloped storage system of the udder is not excessively overloaded, but that the "loading" of the reflex mechanisms that regulate the tone of the motor apparatus is gradually increased. As a general rule one can say that three milkings will be the optimum for the majority of these cows. At the same time two milkings may be quite permissible for cows with a well-developed and trained storage function, even although their milk productivity may be considerably higher than that of young or newly-calved cows. It stands to reason that there is no sense in milking cows whose productivity is low more than twice a day when there is no reason to expect that their productivity will increase. This question will be dealt with separately in Chapter V.

Some aspects of the storage function of the mammary gland still need to be clarified in greater detail. The problem of variations in this function both in successive lactations and in the course of a single lactation in relation to variations in the intensity of milk secretion as the lactation curve falls off is of particular theoretical and practical interest. There are data to show that the capacity of the udder undergoes basic alterations in the course of a single lactation in relation to increase or decline in the milk productivity of the animal. According to Beguchev (1950), the capacity of the udder is fairly constant in the first half of the lactation; capacity declines from the fifth to the seventh month, but more slowly in non-pregnant than in pregnant cows. By the end of the lactation the period required for complete filling of the udder increases to 20 or more hours as compared with 10–12 hr. at the beginning of

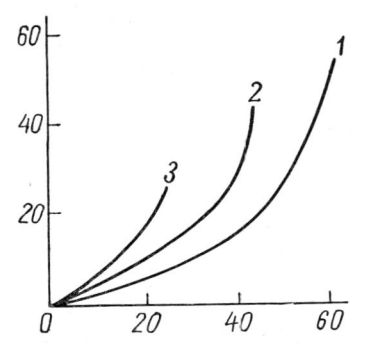

FIG. 14. Dependence of intramammary pressure on the extent to which the storage system is filled. (From Turner, 1955a.)

1, 2, 3—beginning, middle and end of the lactation of one cow. X-axis—milk yield (lb.); y-axis—pressure (cm. of water).

the lactation. According to Beguchev, this is one of the expressions of the varying intensity in the secretion of milk at different periods in the lactation. If this is so the intensity of secretion clearly declines more rapidly towards the end of the lactation than does the reduction of udder capacity.

Azimov (1956) connects variations in udder capacity in the course of the lactation with the new formation or, conversely, with the involution of considerable areas of secretory tissue. Both these processes are observed throughout the whole course of the lactation, but one may considerably predominate at a given period.

Turner (1955a) obtained data of fundamental importance on variations in the capacity of the udder and in intramammary pressure in the course of lactation. Like a number of his predecessors (Beguchev, 1950; Zaks and Pavlov, 1952; Nikitin et al., 1953; Tverdun and Doktorovich, 1953, and others), he concluded that there was no direct linear relationship between udder filling and the magnitude of intramammary pressure. Fig. 14 shows this quite clearly. Nevertheless, the ratios between the accumulation of milk, i.e., the extent to which the storage system of the udder is filled, and the level of intramammary pressure take on a quite different expression at different periods in the lactation. At the beginning of the lactation, "critical pressure", i.e., the pressure level at which secretion is affected, is reached when the udder is a great deal fuller than at the close of the lactation. Thus, in one cow, critical pressure was reached at the beginning of the lactation after 60 lb. (27 kg.) of milk had accumulated in the udder, but after 40 lb. had accumulated in the middle of the lactation and after 20 lb. at the close. The author explains this circumstance simply by the purely anatomical reduction of the udder capacity. In view of the considerations outlined above one can scarcely agree with this opinion and one must conclude that physiological causes play a no less important role. One proof of this is undoubtedly Turner's own data, which show that not only is udder capacity altered at different stages in the lactation, but that the level of critical pressure takes on new values. For example, in one of the cows secretion was almost unimpeded at the beginning of the lactation at a pressure of 20 cm. of water, but greatly depressed when the pressure reached and exceeded 40 cm. At the close of the lactation milk synthesis was almost totally halted at a pressure of 20 cm. Thus, the "resistivity" of secretory activity to the retarding effect of pressure progressively declines in the course of the lactation. Quite apart from its fundamental practical importance, especially for the drying off of cows, this fact is of purely experimental interest, since its further analysis may help to clarify a number of the connexions between the secretion and accumulation of milk.

According to Kulikov (1959), there is a decline in the relative volume of the cisternal portion and the residual milk in the second half of the lactation, when the fat content of the former increases and of the latter declines. There is a relative increase in alveolar volume.

CHAPTER TWO

THE PHYSIOLOGY OF MILK EJECTION

Concepts defined. We must first define certain concepts and delineate the main phenomena that take place when the mammary gland is evacuated in the process of milking or suckling. No unified terminology for these phenomena has yet been established in either Soviet or foreign literature. We use "molokootdacha", "molokovyvedenie", "molokovydelenie", "molokootdelenie" and similar terms as synonyms for "let down of the milk" and "ejection of the milk", which are used in English language publications. I shall continue to use the term "molokootdacha" (translated as "milk ejection" throughout—*Translator*), which occurs most commonly in our literature on physiology and animal husbandry. But we are more concerned with the meaning that should be given to the term than with the term itself. The very concepts of milk secretion and removal have long been inadequately restricted and there has often been and sometimes still is a certain confusion in the concepts. It has to be said that at the present level of our knowledge it is not always possible to effect a precise demarcation. It would not be entirely correct to describe the act of milk ejection as being exclusively a motor act, i.e., as the process by which the gland is freed of milk which was entirely present in the storage system before milking began: it is certain that a part of the matter in this milk is intensively transferred from the cells into the cavity of the gland in the very process of milking; in other words, there is a secretory as well as a motor component to milk ejection.

Milk ejection is, moreover, an extremely complex act involving a series of reflexes that take place at the same time, each of which fulfils a strictly defined role. The phenomena that occur in the process of milking can be provisionally delineated in the following manner, without as yet considering their intrinsic nature.

1. Preparation for and commencement of milking. The milk that

is already present in the cistern is milked out. All that is required for its removal is to overcome the resistance of the external teat sphincters. The cow's "participation" at this stage is confined to active weakening of the tone of the teat sphincters and, thus, to lowering of their resistance.

2. Continuation of milking. At this time milk from the large calibre ducts, i.e., the next portion to be ready for transfer into the cistern, may be involved, in addition to the milk already in the cistern. This transfer is brought about by active reflex changes in the tone of the musculature of the ducts.

3. Continuation of milking. Milk now enters the ducts and subsequently the cistern as a result of contraction of the alveoli, brought about by a definite neurohumoral reflex.

4. Completion of milking. Additional amounts of milk may here be obtained as a result of the manipulations, such as final massage, which conclude the milking. This milk enters the cisterns as a result of reflex acts identical to those described under paragraph 2 above.

Any such delineation of periods is, of course, schematic; some processes may be superimposed on others under normal conditions.

It is important to make these distinctions, if only because there may be variations in the separate links of this complete process in the act of milk ejection: for example, the various complications and difficulties that are so often encountered in practice when milking certain cows may be due to disturbance of one or other of the links in the motor reaction of the mammary gland, and different approaches may therefore be needed to deal with these disturbances.

All that has been said must be taken into consideration when deciding how to study those reactions of the motor apparatus of the udder that are associated with milk ejection.

Methods for the study of milk ejection. In a study of milk ejection the most fundamental properties are time, i.e., the latent period of milk ejection and the duration of active expulsion (milk ejection rate), the amount of milk expelled (alveolar volume), and, finally, the pressure that develops in the storage system in the process of milk ejection. Only a part of these indices can be observed in normal hand or machine milking. In hand milking the moment at which milk ejection commences can only be established if the cisternal volume is small and is milked out before active milk ejection commences or if the latent period is sufficiently large. Given these conditions, one can even sometimes measure the volume of both the cisternal and the alveolar milk separately. In machine milking these indices can be detected, although admittedly quite approximately, if the milk pail is suspended from a sufficiently sensitive spring balance or placed on the platform of pointer scales: the duration of the latent period of the reflex and the proportions of the cisternal and alveolar volumes can be detected from a time record of the scale readings if the milking out of the one does not overlap with that of the other.

Beck, Frier and Roark (1951) and Whittlestone and Phillips (1951) have designed an apparatus that records the milking curve automatically. Aizenbudas (1957a) has recently suggested an extremely handy apparatus for automatically noting the rate of milk removal, separated into its portions, when using hand and machine milking under farming conditions.

All these methods have the common drawback that one cannot use them to establish the precise moment at which milk ejection commences, although this is of great significance under farming conditions.

It has to be said that even when using a catheter under experimental conditions one can only speak provisionally of the true time at which milk ejection commences in animals with a developed storage system. The "commencement" of milk ejection is taken to be the moment at which milk begins to flow through the catheter. It would be more correct to take this reading from the moment at which the alveoli begin to contract, since the rate at which milk enters the cistern is dependent on a number of prior circumstances, the first of which are the tone and resistance of the ducts. In this case I have to agree with Whittlestone (1952) that, owing to its greatly reduced storage system, the pig is a very convenient subject for an experiment in which the true commencement of milk ejection needs to be noted with particular accuracy (e.g., when testing milk-ejection hormones).

In a number of cases, however, cannulation of the teats (or chronic fistulas) is still the only suitable method. Ordinary veterinary teat cannulas are used on cows for this purpose. For goats it is best to use special plexiglass or metal catheters 1·5–2 mm. in diameter that are well polished and have a blunt conical end; the external end of the catheter is bulbous and a rubber tube can be fitted to it. A catheter can also be made from a stout hypodermic needle by cutting off and blunting the pointed end. It is better if a tapering circular sleeve is soldered on to this needle 8–10 mm. from the tip. This sleeve passes through the sphincter and prevents the catheter from falling out. Permanent fistulas of the teat are also used in goats. Grachev (1951a) introduced the fistula tube into an incision in the teat wall near the base. Tsakhaev (1951) used a fistula tube introduced through an incision in the teat wall at the natural opening—the teat canal, in which it is retained by a special enlargement. Fistulas of this type can be maintained for weeks.

Prolonged drainage of the cistern in goats is much more conveniently effected by Tverskoi's tapering catheters (1955a), which are inserted in the teat canal and can remain there for a long time. Slight pressure is all that is necessary to remove the catheter when desired.

Various precautions, especially meticulous disinfection of the catheters and tubes attached to them, must be observed to prevent mastitis. The catheter is smeared before insertion with sterile vaseline or, preferably, with penicillin ointment (10,000 units of penicillin in 10·0 g. of sterile vaseline). One must be careful to avoid injury to the aperture of the teat canal and the canal itself when inserting the catheter; when removing the catheter a small quantity of milk (approximately 30 ml.) must always be left in the cistern and subsequently milked out by hand. If possible, the same teat should not be catheterized more than once in two days. If all the precautions are observed teats can be catheterized indefinitely without harm to the animal. I have had cases in which a catheter was inserted at every milking over a period of some months into a teat that was difficult to milk. The catheter was inserted by a milkmaid who had been thoroughly instructed in the procedure. Nevertheless, one must take particular care when using a catheter for experimental purposes under farming conditions and "overprecaution" is clearly justified, for obvious reasons. In first experiments the insertion of the catheter may inhibit the motor reactions of the mammary gland in some cows, especially if the insertion is carried out by a person not known to the animal. The main experiments should therefore be preceded by a period in which the animal is accustomed to the catheter.

The procedure employed when studying milk ejection with the aid of a catheter can be outlined as follows: (1) the catheter is inserted or the fistula tube is opened; (2) the cisternal portion of the milk is drained off and its volume is measured; (3) stimuli sufficient to cause milk ejection are applied (the nature of the stimuli will be discussed below); (4) the presence or absence of milk discharge from the ducts before removal of the alveolar portion is noted; the moment at which the alveolar portion begins to be removed through the catheter and the duration of its flow, etc., are recorded with a stop watch; (5) hand stripping is carried out after the catheter has been removed and the volume of the strippings from the catheterized quarter of the udder is measured; this is preceded by various manipulations (such as massage and washing the udder with warm water) that stimulate removal of this additional portion of milk.

This outline may, of course, be modified in relation to the object of the research.

In addition to the visual method, one can also use G. N. Pavlov's graphic method (1955b). A rubber tube is fitted to the free end of the catheter and attached to a glass stopcock, the free end of which is drawn out and bent downwards. Before the test the apparatus is filled with water from the catheter to the end of the stopcock. Drops of water and then of milk fall on to the balance arm of a special drop recorder and their weight closes a mercury contact in a circuit containing an ordinary electromagnetic marker (Fig. 15). This records the fall of each drop on a kymographic tracing.

The study of milk ejection sometimes entails observation of changes in intracisternal pressure. For this purpose one uses an ordinary vertical manometer, consisting of a T-shaped tube mounted on a wooden stand with a centimetre scale. The vertical branch, which is 60–70 cm. long, is placed with its open end uppermost. One of the horizontal branches is fitted with a stopcock and the other is connected with the catheter by a rubber tube of suitable length. The manometer is zeroed at the base level of the teat. The stopcock is closed when the catheter is inserted. The milk rises in the manometer to a level that corresponds to the pressure in the cistern. The stopcock is then opened and the cisternal milk is drained off, after which the stopcock is closed. After milking commences the onset of milk ejection and all pressure changes that occur during it may be recorded. Specially designed spring manometers have also been successfully used for this purpose by Nikitin, Tverdun and Doktorovich (1953) and later by Syusyukin (1955).

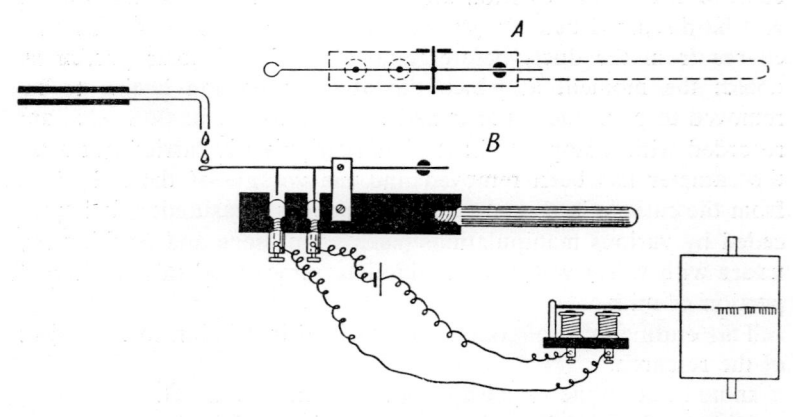

FIG. 15. Diagram of the drop-recording device. (From Pavlov, 1955b.)
A—view from above; *B*—circuit for the recording of drops of milk.

A small Marey's tambour with a membrane of rubber from a thin surgical glove is used for graphic recording of cisternal pressure. The membrane is calibrated in the normal manner from the readings of a mercury or water manometer. A three-way cock, through which milk can be drawn off if required, and a two-necked flask, to prevent milk flowing into the capsule when there is a considerable rise in pressure, are fitted to the tube that connects the capsule with the catheter.

The difficulties of studying milk ejection in laboratory animals are well known. The method based on a single suckling is used to determine the amount of milk given by rabbits (Cross and Harris, 1952). The doe is removed from the young 7–14 days after their birth and returned to them once or twice a day. The offspring are weighed on accurate scales immediately before and after feeding and the amount of milk given is assessed from the difference in weight. This method can only give an approximate idea of the efficiency of milk ejection, since milk from the sinuses is also suckled.

Fine catheters can be inserted in the teat canal of guinea-pigs if the animals are suitably restrained (Baryshnikov et al., 1951). Cross and Harris have also used this technique on rabbits, by inserting a fine glass tube into one of the milk passages they were able to record the pressure of milk ejection with a sensitive piston recorder. Whittlestone (1954c) has used a similar method to record intramammary pressure in sows.

Microscopic examination of the mammary gland of live mice, a method first proposed by Glebina (1940), provides great scope for the direct observation of contractions in the ducts and alveoli. Levitskaya (1955) states that it is best to use mice in the 20th day of lactation. The mouse is lightly anaesthetized with ether and fastened to a glass plate of suitable size for mounting on the microscope stage. The second inguinal gland is prepared for the observations. The fur around the areola of the teat concerned is removed with tweezers. The ridge of skin that surrounds the periphery of the areola is transfixed by two fine threads arranged caudally and cranially with respect to each other. Fine vascular needles are used for the sewing. A circular incision is then made on the outside of the ridge of skin surrounding the areola with a sharp knife and the wound is extended towards the head and tail by small linear incisions. Slight traction is applied to the fixing threads and the piece of skin with the teat and the gland is blunt dissected from the subcutaneous fascia. Pressure on the threads is then further increased and the gland is drawn outwards. The gland is spread out and fastened with threads and fine entomological pins to the edges of a circular cork washer fixed to the glass with paraffin wax or Mendeleev's cement. One must avoid damage to the gland and ensure that the blood vessels are not twisted or constricted. The prepared animal is then placed on the microscope stage and is examined in transmitted light. The mount is moistened from time to time with warm Ringer's solution. This method has already yielded many important new facts when used in conjunction with photomicrography and ciné-photomicrography.

Another method for studying the motor function of the mammary gland that is undoubtedly very promising is the radiographic study of the storage system of the udder, that has recently been proposed by Bílek and Janovský (1955). A catheter, which is subsequently withdrawn, is used to introduce 20 ml. of a 35% solution of a contrast medium (ultraren), heated to 37°C, into the cistern. An equal amount of milk is removed from the cistern before introduction of the medium. Changes in the configuration of the cistern and ducts filled with the medium and the mixing of the medium can then be traced by X-ray examination and especially X-ray photography (Fig. 16).

The reflex arc of milk ejection. Milk ejection is an intricate complex reflex reaction of the motor apparatus of the udder that develops in response to adequate stimuli of the skin of the teats and udder. Sufficient experimental material has now been accumulated to enable us to give a fairly precise description of the separate links in this reaction and of the process as a whole in relation to both morphology and physiology.

The afferent fibres of the reflex arc of milk ejection originate in receptors in the teats and udder and lead into the mixed spinal nerves; in cows and goats their main mass enters the trunk of the external spermatic nerve. When all the nerves of one half of the udder in goats are severed (Tsakhaev, 1953), the milk ejection reflex declines on the denervated side but is fully retained on the other side. Under these conditions adequate stimuli of the normal side also give rise to milk ejection on the denervated side, but this is now due to the humoral link of the reflex.

The subsequent course of the afferent fibres associated with the act of milk ejection has been studied in G. N. Pavlov's experiments (Baryshnikov *et al.*, 1953). Buried electrodes were first placed in the trunk of the external spermatic nerve in the lumbar region at a short distance from the point of its emergence from lumbar nerve roots. A mandrin with a nylon thread round the nerve was fixed at a point distal to the electrodes. After the goat had recovered from the operation the thread was sharply pulled out, thus immediately severing the nerve. There was a sharp but brief pain reaction to severance; it is interesting to note that there was an energetic discharge of milk from both teats at the moment of severance and that this reaction was, to all appearances, indistinguishable from natural milk ejection developing in response to adequate stimuli of the teats. It was also possible to obtain a typical milk-ejection reaction on both sides by stimulating the central end of the nerve with an induction current. An example of an experiment of this type is shown in Fig. 17.

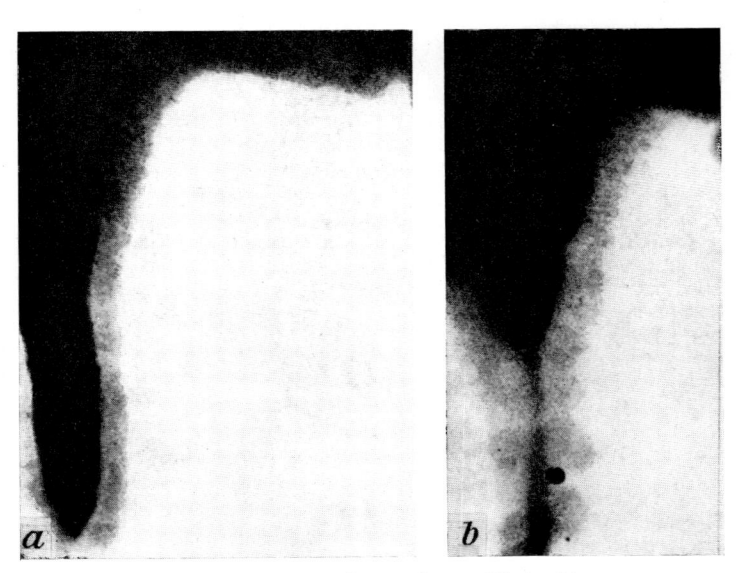

FIG. 16. X-ray photograph of teat cistern filled with a contrast medium. (From Bílek and Janovský, 1955.)

a—atonic cistern; *b*—cistern contracted.

(Photographs by courtesy of Dr. J. Bílek.)

The strength of stimulating current required to obtain a milk-ejection reaction was not sufficient to give rise to any reaction of pain in the animal. Milk ejection could be induced, whenever the udder was sufficiently full, over a period of several days, till the electrodes became grown over with connective tissue.

A more precise study of the nature of the afferent fibres associated with the milk ejection reflex is of especially great interest in relation to whether these pathways are specialized for the milk-ejection reaction or whether the impulses that exercise reflex control over milk removal and those that maintain its secretion make use of the same afferent pathway.

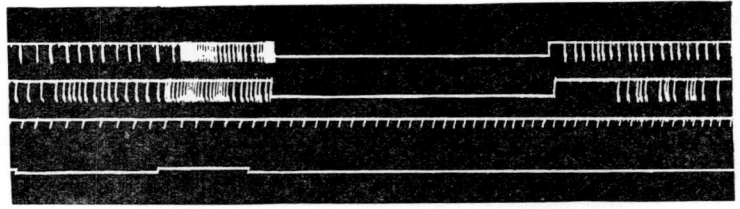

FIG. 17. Milk ejection of a goat when the central end of the external spermatic nerve is stimulated. (From Baryshnikov *et al.*, 1953.) Reading from above: drops of milk from right teat, from left teat, time scale 5 sec., indication of stimulus.

Any attempt to separate these pathways in mixed peripheral nerve trunks would undoubtedly come up against insurmountable difficulties. Tsakhaev used another approach to this end. His method was to partially sever the spinal cord where, as is known, the separate ascending pathways are topographically well demarcated. When a half (Brown-Séquard) section was made in the right half of the spinal cord at the level of the eleventh or twelfth thoracic vertebra, the typical Brown-Séquard syndrome of motor and sensory disturbances developed and the milk-ejection reflex declined on the side of the transection. Milk secretion remained at almost the initial level. This experiment showed quite clearly that the conductors associated with milk ejection passed through the dorsal columns of the spinal cord, the fibres of which are known to ascend without crossing over as far as the nuclei of Goll and Burdach in the medulla oblongata, where they terminate.

This conclusion was confirmed by a number of other transections.

In one goat the dorsal columns were severed from the left in addition to Brown-Séquard half section of the spinal column from the right. This caused a decline in the milk-ejection reflex from both sides; signs of ataxia, that are typical when muscular sensibility is impaired, developed simultaneously in the hind quarters. In this animal milk secretion not only remained at its former level but began to increase three weeks after the operation and soon exceeded the initial level by 80%.

In one goat the dorsal columns were severed from both sides while the other pathways were preserved whole, and this led to a decline in the milk-ejection reflex on both sides; milk secretion was maintained at the initial level and exceeded this level within a month of the operations.

Apart from the main conclusion that the afferent pathways of milk ejection follow "their own" side in the dorsal columns, these experiments give rise to another most important conclusion: milk removal and regulation of its secretion are associated with different afferent pathways; secretion may be both maintained and, under certain conditions, increased when there is a total falling off in the milk-ejection reflex. One case cited by Tsakhaev is typical from this point of view. Brown-Séquard section of the spinal cord from the right was carried out on one of the goats in the experiment. The operation gave rise to a destructive process which caused additional damage across the spinal cord. It was discovered at autopsy that an extensive focus of softening had developed at the level of the transection from the left-hand side; both the dorsal columns and a considerable part of the dorsal horn and the lateral columns had been destroyed. Persistent disturbances developed in the animal almost immediately after the operation: there was almost total motor paralysis of the rear half of the body, but connexion was not totally severed since there was still slight general reaction to sufficiently strong stimuli of the hind quarters and certain, admittedly slight, spontaneous movements in the hind quarters. The milk-ejection reflex was absent from both halves of the udder. There was a great decline in milk secretion immediately after the operation (to 10% of the initial level), but it subsequently began to be re-established and reached the initial level by the 10th day and exceeded it on the 26th day. Thus secretion can be maintained even when there has been considerable damage to a cross-section of the spinal cord. The subsequent course of the afferent pathways of milk ejection is still not quite clear. It is not known whether they are interrupted, like other fibres of the dorsal columns, in the nuclei of Goll and Burdach in the medulla oblongata. Their subsequent course in the brain stem has, however, been established by Andersson (1951b), who has shown that isolated stimulation of the fibres of the medial lemniscus immediately in front of the inferior olive causes milk ejection in both the normal and the denervated halves of the udder. These fibres then ascend farther up the brain stem to the region of the anterior hypothalamus, where the afferent pathway of the unconditioned reflex arc of milk ejection terminates.

It may now be considered as firmly established that the central sector of this arc is located in the supraoptic nucleus. In chronic experiments Andersson implanted electrodes in the region of the supraoptic nuclei, and later checked the accuracy with which they had been positioned by histological examination of the brain. Stimulation always caused a flow of milk through the catheter, that was to all appearances indistinguishable from normal milk ejection.

In some tests stimulation of the region of the supraoptic nuclei caused a general pain reaction in the animal as well as milk ejection. In these cases the effect of milk ejection was somewhat less marked, as if inhibited. This phenomenon was scarcely perceptible in the denervated half of the gland, but clearly defined on the side where normal innervation was preserved. This shows that inhibition is associated in this case with direct nervous influences on the tone of the ducts and not with any hormonal effects.

Milk removal was only observed when the electrodes were accurately situated: stimulation of hypothalamic regions adjacent to the supraoptic nuclei did not give rise to milk ejection. It should be noted that an area was discovered immediately adjacent to the supraoptic nucleus, stimulation of which evoked rumination. This circumstance is certainly of interest in relation to the findings of Grachev (1953a), Orlov (1955) and Azimov (1955) that the rumination reflex can easily be produced by stimulating the teats and udder. This discovery led these authors to draw a number of conclusions concerning close functional connexions between the functions of lactation and digestion.

In a later paper Andersson and McCann (1955) further clarified the location of the hypothalamic centre of milk ejection in goats.

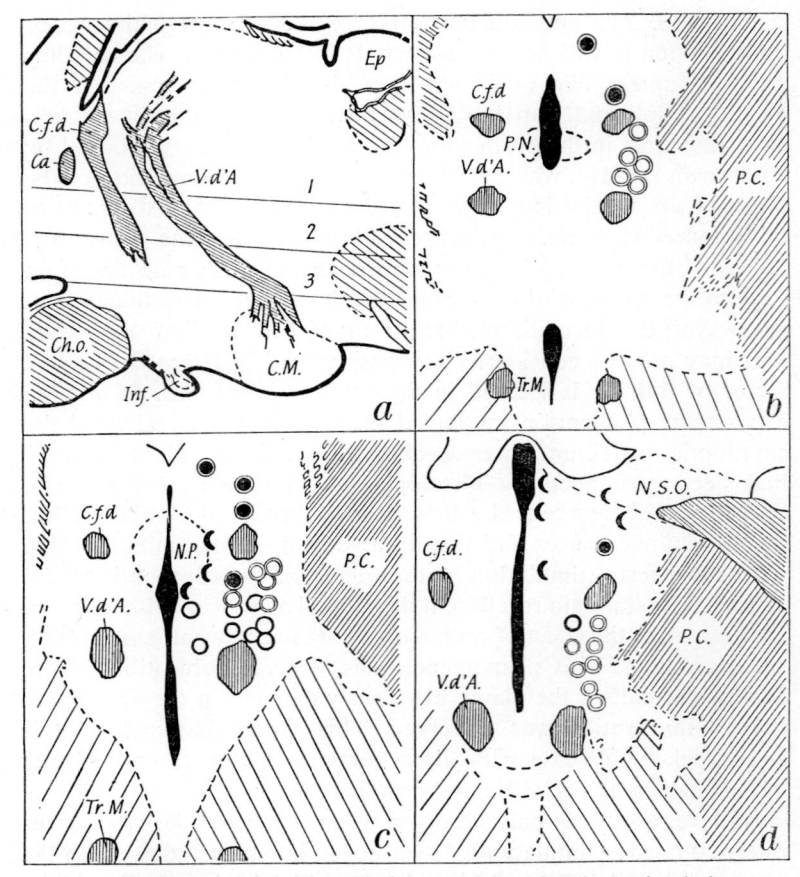

FIG. 18. Points in the hypothalamus where electrical stimulation evoked drinking, antidiuresis and milk ejection.

Diagrams of a sagittal section, and, corresponding to the lines labelled 1, 2 and 3, three horizontal sections (1, 2 and 3) through the hypothalamus of the goat.

Black circles: Points where electrical stimulation caused drinking, inhibition of water diuresis and milk ejection.

Open circles: Points where drinking was obtained in the absence of antidiuresis and milk ejection.

Black half moons: Points where stimulation gave inhibition of water diuresis and milk ejection, but no drinking.

C. A.	= Commissura anterior.	N. P.	= Nucleus paraventricularis.
C. f. d.	= Columna fornicis descendens.	N. S .O.	= Nucleus supraopticus.
C. M.	= Corpus mammillare.	P. C.	= Pedunculus cerebri.
Ch. O.	= Chiasma opticum.	Tr. M.	= Tractus Meynert.
Ep.	= Epiphysis.	V. d'A.	= Tractus Vicq d'Ayzr.
Inf.	= Infundibulum.		

(From Andersson and McCann, 1955.)

They confirmed Andersson's previous data on the connexion between milk ejection and the supraoptic nuclei and established that stimulation of these nuclei invariably inhibits diuresis, in addition to evoking milk ejection. When certain adjacent areas of the hypothalamus are stimulated these two effects are accompanied by excessive thirst, as a result of which the goat will drink 5 litres or more of water at a time in direct response to the stimulus (Fig. 18).

Using Andersson's method, Popovich (1958) has shown that when the supraoptic nucleus is stimulated in goats the magnitude of milk ejection is dependent on the strength and duration of the stimulus. If the stimulus is weak milk ejection can be obtained with ease several times in the course of the same experiment; this shows that the oxytocin can be secreted in portions. Tsakhaev's findings on the possible "fractionation" of milk ejection in goats can clearly be explained in this manner. When half the udder is denervated the effect of stimulation of the supraoptic nucleus is manifest on both sides, but more rapidly on the denervated side. When there is simultaneous stimulation of the supraoptic nucleus, causing milk ejection, and of a point in the posterior hypothalamus, causing defecation, both these reactions are inhibited. Unlike a similar experiment by Cross (1955a) in which stimulation was applied in the region of the paraventricular nucleus, the injection of oxytocin induces milk ejection under these conditions. Popovich considers that this inhibitory effect is not associated with the discharge of adrenaline, as in Cross' experiment, but with delay in the secretion of oxytocin. After destruction of one of the supraoptic nuclei by electrocoagulation, milk ejection declines on the side of the destruction and is maintained on the intact side. After some time the reflex is partially rehabilitated on the side of the destruction.

The descending pathways from the supraoptic nuclei have been traced by Cross and Harris (1952). They were able to show from experiments on rabbits that direct stimulation of the supraopticohypophysial tract caused milk ejection. The subsequent course of these pathways has been established by Jacobsohn (1949). She has shown that severance of the pituitary stalk, through which all the main pathways that connect the neural lobe with the hypothalamic centre are known to pass, causes persistent decline in milk ejection.

The significance to milk ejection of the nervous connexions of the neurohypophysis has been demonstrated by Harris and

Jacobsohn (1952) in a more complicated experiment. A hypophysial graft was effected in the region of the medial eminence of the hypothalamus in hypophysectomized rats. The graft restored fertility; pregnancy and birth caused the onset of lactation, but the young died of hunger, since milk ejection was impossible. It is true that this result is not absolutely unequivocal: it may equally well point to the absence of the milk-ejection reflex and to profound degeneration of the neurohypophysis of the type known to occur when its nervous connexions with the supraoptic nuclei of the hypothalamus are interrupted.

New data on rehabilitation of the milk-ejection reflex after section of the pituitary stalk have been independently obtained by Tverskoi (1959, 1960a, 1960b) and Tsakhaev (1959a). The milk-ejection reflex declines after section of the pituitary stalk in goats. It begins to recover slowly after 10–14 days, but still remains far below the normal level. Histological examination shows signs of hypertrophy to the central end of the stump of the severed pituitary stalk, where a formation histologically similar to the neural lobe of the pituitary develops (Tverskoi). It is possible that the rehabilitation of the reflex is associated with a regenerative process of this type.

The fibres from the supraoptic nuclei that pass through the pituitary stalk terminate in its neural portion. The impulses that arrive along these fibres cause the discharge of the corresponding hormonal substance. This is the commencement of a new, hormonal link in the milk-ejection reflex. The detailed exposition called for by the nature and essence of hormonal effects in milk ejection will be given a little later. In relation to the efferent nerves of the motor apparatus of the mammary gland, the majority of authors consider that they are purely sympathetic and are mainly connected with the 2nd, 3rd and 4th lumbar ganglia of the sympathetic nerve trunk (Espe, 1946; Bogdashev and Eliseev, 1951), but it is clearly not possible to exclude the sacral ganglia of the sympathetic nerve from participation in the motor innervation of the udder. It is therefore desirable to extirpate both the sacral and the lumber ganglia in experiments in which the maximum sympathetic denervation of the gland is required.

The existence of parasympathetic innervation of the mammary gland is still denied by the majority of investigators. At any rate Linzell (1950) and Peeters, Coussens and Sierens (1949) have concluded from pharmacological analysis of the efferent innervation of the mammary gland that the synaptic junctions and postganglionic neurons typical of the parasympathetic system are absent from the parenchyma of the mammary gland.

Thus the neurological aspect of the arc of the unconditioned milk-ejection reflex has been studied in considerable detail. The same cannot yet be said of the cortical representation of the reflex. The physiological role of the cortex of the cerebral hemispheres in milk removal has been shown by experimental work and by countless empirical observations. Nevertheless, there is still no clarity on the pathways that connect the subcortical centres of milk ejection with the cerebral cortex or on the localization of this function in the cortex, and the subject is in need of further study.

Nikitin's work (1905) still remains the only basic attempt to resolve this difficult question and to ascertain the location in the cerebral cortex of the hypothetical lactation centre that is assumed to exist by Grachev (1953) and many others. It must, however, be stated that although the physiological existence of such a centre is not disputed, it certainly need not have the strict anatomical location assigned to it by Nikitin. Full weight should be given to I. P. Pavlov's detailed criticism of Nikitin's work.

The outline of the regulation of milk ejection given in Fig. 19 is based on the materials already examined. This outline was first developed by a group, of which I was a member, in the Laboratory of Physiology of Farm Animals of the Pavlov Physiological Institute (U.S.S.R. Academy of Sciences). It is here given in a slightly revised form.

Impulses from the receptors of the teats and udder reach the spinal cord via the afferent fibres of the posterior roots (I), and from there can be transmitted along the collaterals (II) to the motor apparatus of the udder, by using the corresponding vegetative neurons (III) as efferent pathways. This is the "short" arc, which is responsible for a number of the simple segmental reactions of the motor apparatus of the udder, primarily connected with regulation of its tone. Having given rise to the collaterals indicated, the afferent fibres associated with milk ejection ascend the spinal cord as part of the dorsal trunks to the medulla oblongata. The termination of these pathways in the nuclei of the medulla oblongata is shown hypothetically in the outline. The fibres then reach, by way of the medial lemniscus, the diencephalon, where they terminate in the cells of the supraoptic nuclei (N.S.O.). This point is the commencement of the efferent pathway (VI), which passes via the supraoptico-hypophysial tract and the pituitary stalk to the posterior pituitary

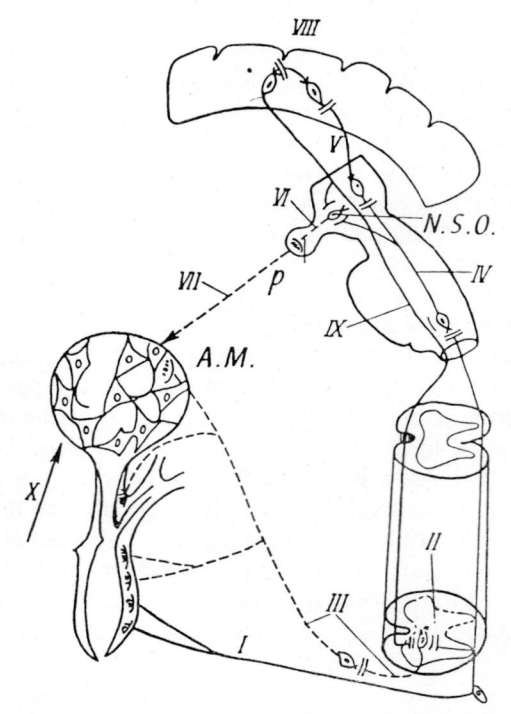

Fig. 19. Diagram of reflex regulation of milk ejection.

(p.p.). Here the impulses that arrive along the efferent fibres stimulate the discharge of a hormone which operates humorally, through the blood (VII), to effect contraction of the alveolar myoepithelium (A.M.). This is an outline of the unconditioned reflex arc of milk ejection. The whole outline has, as has already been stated, an experimental foundation. The only hypothetical points in the outline are the termination in the nuclei of the medulla oblongata and the existence of direct efferent innervation of the alveolar myoepithelium (A.M.). It must be stated that Linzell (1950, 1952) did not detect synapses actually on the myoepithelial cells in histological examination, although his neurohistological methods enabled him to demonstrate nerve endings in blood vessels in the same mounts. Linzell lays great stress on the extremely close contact between the capillaries and the myoepithelium and categorically denies any possibility of the direct role of efferent innervation of the alveolar myoepithelium in the regulation of its activity. His argument is hardly convincing, however: this is far from being the first occasion when there has been no morphological confirmation of the existence of direct innervation when physiological considerations provide grounds for assuming that it exists. The same is true, for example, of vasodilatory innervation, the existence of which can scarcely be doubted even although no one has as yet seen the endings of vasodilators in vessels.

The cortical section of the arc as shown in the outline is, as has already been stated, hypothetical. One can assume the existence of pathways (V) that link the hypothalamic centres of milk ejection with the cerebral cortex. Impulses arriving from the mammary gland reach the cortex (VIII) by these pathways where they are analysed. It is here that the many temporary connexions in the activity of the mammary gland, and especially in milk ejection, are established. The cortex maintains control of all the links in the unconditioned reflex arc of milk ejection via the descending pathways (IX).

It is not claimed that the outline is either universal in application or absolutely complete. It is assumed, however, that it can be used in its present form to explain a number of facts which will be encountered in the physiological analysis of milk ejection and when constructing a theory of milk ejection. One advantage of the outline is that it poses a number of new questions for further investigation.

One further addition must be made to the outline. Recent findings (Cross, 1954; Zaks, Olenov and Makeeva, 1956) show that the alveolar myoepithelium responds to direct mechanical stimulation and that this is a significant factor in milk removal. The relevant information will be given in detail below (p. 83). In our outline these influences have been symbolized by a thick arrow (X).

Hormonal factors of milk ejection. Impulses which reach the neurohypophysis cause secretion of a hormonal substance in it which reaches the udder in the blood stream and stimulates contraction of the elements involved in the act of milk ejection.

Ott and Scott (1910), Gavin (1913) and Voskresenskii (1917) were the first to demonstrate that parenteral injection of neurohypophysial extracts into lactating animals and man (Schafer, 1913) can cause the expulsion of milk in a manner similar to the normal reaction to milking or suckling, but these discoveries did not lead

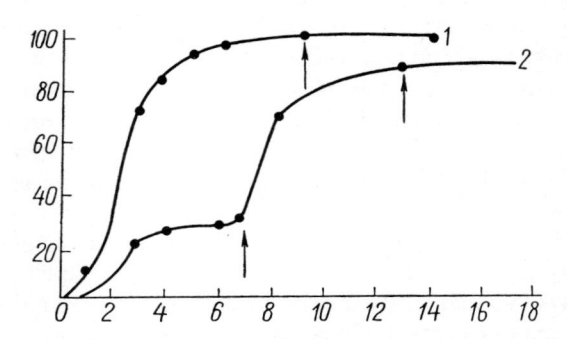

FIG. 20. Suckling of milk by puppies under normal conditions (*1*) and during narcosis of the bitch (*2*). (From Gaines, 1915.)

X-axis—time from beginning of feeding (min.); *y-axis*—increase in weight of pups in course of suckling (g.). Arrows: at left of *2*—moment of injection of posterior pituitary extract; at right of *1* and *2*—moment when evacuation of the gland is completed.

at the time to further developments of the concept of milk ejection as a neurohumoral reflex. It is interesting to note that Gaines (1915) had by this time obtained facts from one of his experiments which would have provided the basis for this conclusion. He demonstrated that the normal rate of evacuation of the mammary gland in a bitch being suckled by pups is greatly inhibited if the bitch is anaesthetised with ether and that it can be rapidly restored by intravenous injection of posterior-pituitary extract (Fig. 20). Nevertheless, Gaines concluded from his experiments that the reflex was purely nervous. I agree with Folley (1954) that it was the absence of developed concepts of neuro-endocrine interrelationships at this time that prevented Gaines from drawing correct conclusions.

Twenty-five years later, Ely and Petersen (1941) confirmed the main fact established by their predecessors and linked the effect of posterior-pituitary extracts on the mammary gland with the oxytocic substances that they contained. They also established that the administration of blood, taken from a cow at the moment of milk ejection, to another cow which is not being milked causes milk removal. A similar effect is obtained if such blood is passed through the vessels of an isolated, milk-filled udder. Andersson (1951c) has shown that blood taken from the jugular vein of a goat immediately after stimulation of the supraoptic nucleus stimulates enhanced removal of milk when injected into another intact animal. In experiments on goats in which one half of the udder had been totally denervated, Tsakhaev (1953) noted that milking of the normal half also caused milk ejection on the denervated side. All these facts can only be explained by the participation of a humoral component in the reaction of milk ejection.

The majority of investigators link this effect with oxytocin, which is one of the hormones present in posterior-pituitary extract.

According to Irving (1944) oxytocin (synonyms—"Pitocin" and "alpha-hypoamine") is a polypeptide containing some 5 amino-acids and possessing active sulphydryl groups; its molecular weight is between 600 and 2000. Oxytocin can be separated from the large "mother molecule" (Irving), which also contains vasopressor and antidiuretic fractions.

The structural formula of oxytocin has recently been established by Du Vigneaud and his colleagues (1953b) and they have since (1953a) succeeding in synthesizing a substance which they call oxytocin S. This substance is a polypeptide (octapeptide) consisting of 8 amino acids: leucine, isoleucine, tyrosine, proline, glutamic acid, aspartic acid, glycine and cystine. When tested on the normal biological test subjects for oxytocin this preparation showed high activity and was in any case no less effective than natural oxytocin in its effect on milk ejection in man (Nickerson *et al.*, 1954). The authors do not, however, definitely conclude that natural oxytocin and oxytocin S are absolutely identical.

Whittlestone (1950) concluded from tests of different fractions of posterior-pituitary extract on pigs that there was a special milk-ejection hormone—the "galactergic" hormone.

According to Ely and Petersen (1941) and Andersson (1951a), the oxytocic fraction of a posterior-pituitary extract ("Pitocin") is more effective in relation to milk ejection than the vasopressor fraction ("Pitressin"). Cross and Harris (1952), however, conclude that oxytocin is more effective if the preparation is somewhat "contaminated" with the general neurohypophysial extract. We have therefore not, as yet, finally settled the true nature of the hormonal substance in the neurohypophysis which takes part in milk ejection.* It is certain that the final solution will be connected to some extent with the more general question of the specificity of the various hormones of the neurohypophysis. In this connexion we must refer to other data, in addition to the findings of Andersson and McCann (1955), Cross (1951) and a number of other authors (Kalliala *et al.*, 1951, 1952; Peeters and Coussens, 1950) report that there is also marked inhibition of diuresis in water-loaded animals during milking or suckling. This phenomenon has been detected in various subjects including the woman, the bitch and the rabbit. Kalliala has established that the decline in diuresis is accompanied by an increase in the movement of sodium and that a decline in diuresis is therefore really associated in this case with the secretion of an antidiuretic hormone. Nevertheless, one can scarcely conclude from these facts that the antidiuretic hormone and the hormone responsible for milk ejection are identical, as do Andersson and McCann. It is easier to agree with Cross, who concludes from a comparison of doses of separate posterior-pituitary fractions, the effect of which is primarily either oxytocic or antidiuretic, that these hormones are different.

Andersson (1951a) found that the injection of a hypertonic solution of NaCl into the carotid artery, i.e., an increase in osmotic pressure in the carotid blood, causes milk ejection. Abrahams and Pickford (1954) have established that this same influence leads to contraction of the uterus, which is a further confirmation that the oxytocic activity of the blood is enhanced. Verney (1947) has demonstrated that the injection of hypertonic solutions into the carotid artery inhibits water diuresis associated with entry into the blood of the antidiuretic hormone of the posterior pituitary.

Noble (1954) has suggested that the liberation of antidiuretic hormone in the act of milk ejection is an expression of a definite connexion between lactation and the excretory function of the organism, between the mammary gland and the kidney: the decline in diuresis after evacuation of the udder, which decreases water loss by the kidneys, cannot help but create favourable conditions for

* In future we shall refer to the milk-ejection hormone as oxytocin, bearing in mind all the comments that have been made.

the output of water by another channel—through the milk. One can accept this view: it should be remembered that in some cases the daily milk yield of a high-yielding cow may exceed its daily output of urine.

Borsuk (1955a) has also published findings which point to the existence of intricate connexions between the functions of lactation and excretion. She has established that there is a considerable increase in the output of chlorides by the kidneys when the capacity system of the udder is at its fullest. This chloride maximum vanishes and the rate of chloride output is evened out if excessive overfilling of the capacity system of the udder is avoided by changes in the method and hours of milking. The mechanism of this phenomenon is still not quite clear, but it is certain that it is one expression of the existence of intricate nervous and neurohumoral links between the mammary gland and the kidney. The question needs further study.

Little is known about the amounts of the hormone that enter the blood in response to milking stimuli. All that one can say is that no perceptible decline or lowering in the oxytocic activity of the neurohypophysis immediately after milking has apparently been observed. According to Dodd (cited by Folley, 1954) no statistically reliable differences could be detected in the oxytocin and vasopressin content of the neurohypophyses of goats killed immediately after milking or 24 hours later. It appears that the amount of hormone to be secreted at a time is so small that it cannot be detected when determining the oxytocic activity of the neurohypophysis by existing methods.

This is indirectly confirmed by experiments on the amount of hormone needed to produce milk ejection. I have found that intravenous injection of as little as 0·001 ml. of an ampoule solution of posterior-pituitary extract (approximately 0·003 i.u.) in goats causes a noticeable increase in milk removal through a catheter. According to Cowie (cited by Folley, 1954), 1 i.u. causes milk removal that is comparable with natural milk ejection (in its effect on intracisternal pressure) in an anaesthetized goat. Cowie states that the goat neurohypophysis contains some 10–15 i.u. of oxytocin; thus approximately 10% of its hormone content is secreted in response to milking. It has to be said that calculations based on figures obtained by this method are extremely approximate. Thus Denamur and Martinet (1953) observed total milk ejection in a goat on the injection of 0·1 i.u. and a threshold effect on the injection of 0·001 i.u. They used the same method as Cowie. The question is clearly in need of further study and it is highly desirable to develop methods for the accurate and rapid determination of the amount of oxytocin in the blood.

There is considerable interest in the speed with which oxytocin becomes effective when injected into the blood, as well as in the subsequent fate of the injected hormone and the reasons for decline in its activity.

The duration of the "latent period" in the hormone's action, i.e., the time between injection and the commencement of the effect, is governed by purely haemodynamic conditions. On intravenous injection of the hormone this time was found to be 13·8 sec. in pigs (Whittlestone) and approximately 19·7 sec. in cows (Peeters and Massart, 1947), i.e., shorter than the normally observed latent period of the reflex contraction of the alveoli (approximately 45 sec.). According to Whittlestone, both the magnitude of the effect and its duration are determined by the size of dose. We now have information which shows that when injected (and, one would suppose, when secreted under natural conditions) the hormone is rapidly destroyed in the blood plasma. According to both Peeters and Petersen and Ludvick (1942), injected hormone is totally destroyed in a cow's blood within half an hour. Page (1946) has isolated a special enzyme—"pitocinase"—from the blood plasma of pregnant women which destroys oxytocin by disrupting its peptide bonds. The amount of "pitocinase" increases sharply towards the close of pregnancy and rapidly declines until it has almost disappeared after birth. Since the significance of "pitocinase" in milking cows, especially during pregnancy, is of undoubted interest, it must be studied in detail.

Thus there can be no doubt that the hormone products of the neurohypophysis are of fundamental significance to the milk-ejection reflex in its final efferent link. According to Ely and Petersen (1941), oxytocin and adrenaline play a primary role in bringing about milk ejection. In our suggested outline oxytocin discharged from the posterior pituitary under the influence of nervous impulses reaches the udder by a humoral path and there causes overall contraction of all the motor elements of both the myoepithelium

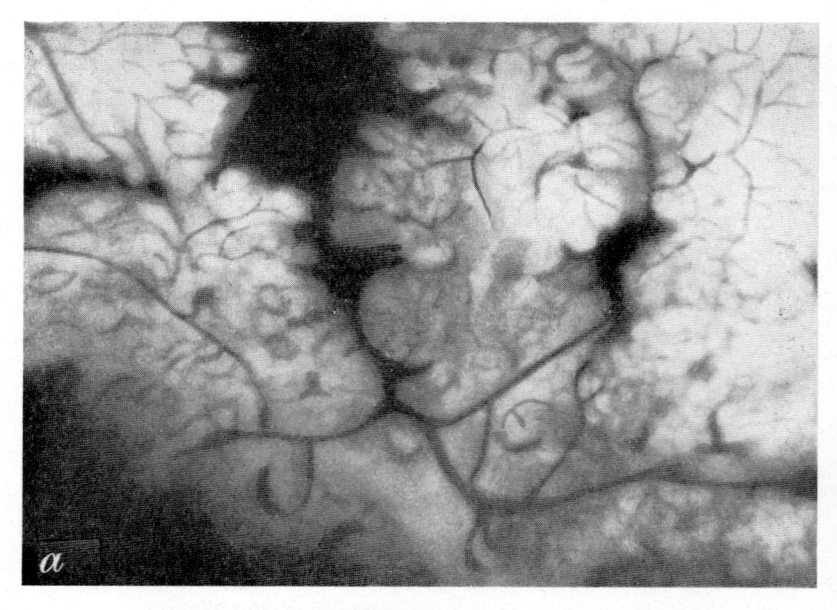

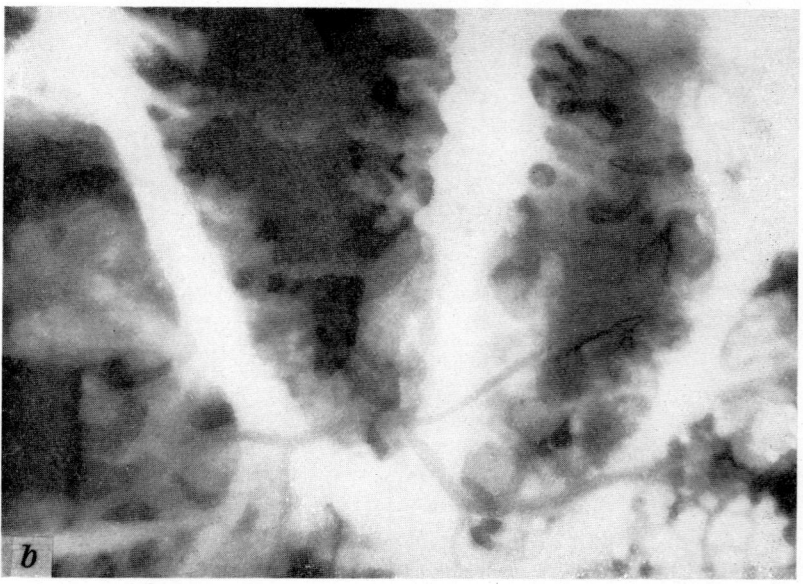

FIG. 21. Mammary gland of mouse. Contraction of alveoli due to posterior-pituitary extract.

a—initial state; *b*—considerable contraction of a large part of the alveoli, ducts dilated and filled with milk.

and the smooth musculature of the ducts, as a result of which milk is expelled into the cistern. In this outline adrenaline is an oxytocin antagonist which, unlike the latter, causes relaxation of all the motor elements of the udder, thus inhibiting its evacuation.

Folley (1954) puts forward a similar view. In his opinion adrenaline may impede realization of the specific effect of oxytocin peripherally, in the mammary gland itself. It is true that Folley does not here exclude the possibility that adrenaline may have a negative effect on the very secretion of oxytocin in the neurohypophysis. We shall find it worth while to return to the possible significance of adrenaline in milk ejection in a slightly different aspect at a later stage. Thus, in the outline of Ely and Petersen, no significance at all is ascribed to efferent innervation of the udder.

We are now, however, in possession of facts which show that direct efferent innervation of the motor apparatus of the udder undoubtedly plays a part in milk ejection. Tsakhaev (1953) has shown that the function of the motor apparatus of the udder is substantially disturbed in the denervated half of an udder. These disturbances are revealed by an increase in the capacity of the alveolar section, shortening of the latent period of the milk-ejection reflex and an increase in the reactivity of the denervated half of the udder to subcutaneous injection of posterior-pituitary extract. However, the fundamental objection to the view of Ely and Petersen is that only the contractile elements of the alveoli react to posterior-pituitary extract, whilst the musculature of the ducts, cistern and sphincter is generally insensitive to it.

Levitskaya (1955) has studied the effect of posterior-pituitary extract and adrenaline on the motor apparatus of the mammary gland by vital microscopy of the lactating gland in a mouse. There was a sharp contraction in the lumen of the ducts, proceeding as far as total closure, 5–15 sec. after the application of adrenaline (1×10^{-5}) to the surface of the mount. A few seconds after the application of an ampoule solution of posterior-pituitary extract ($1 \times 10^{-4} - 2 \times 10^{-5}$) to the mount there was considerable dilatation of the ducts and very marked contraction of the alveoli and the ducts became filled with secretion. Levitskaya stresses that dilatation of the ducts commences slightly before contraction of the alveoli can be discerned (Fig. 21); she considers that dilatation of the ducts is associated with the special effect of the hormone on their smooth musculature and is not due to passive distension by the secretion entering from the alveoli.

Linzell (1955) has fully confirmed the correctness of Levitskaya's hypothesis in a somewhat specialized form of the experiment. He removed the greater part of the young for several days before the experiment, so that some lobes of the gland underwent quite considerable involution. In the microscopic examination of the living animal the alveoli in the glandular areas under consideration were almost empty. Linzell established by topical application of oxytocin that there was dilatation of the ducts even although no milk could enter them from the alveoli. We thus have reason to consider that variations in the diameter of the ducts are here an active process that is associated with contraction of the myoepithelial cells situated along the length of the finest calibre ducts, described by Richardson (1949). In any case, this is the role that is ascribed to these formations by Whittlestone (1950), who also assumed that contraction of the longitudinal myoepithelial cells causes shortening and simultaneous dilatation of the fine ducts and thus facilitates the evacuation of the alveoli.

Tverskoi (1955b) studied the excitability of the smooth musculature of the walls of different sections of the storage system by preparing strips of the teat sphincter and the walls of the cistern and large calibre ducts from a freshly killed cow. He found that the musculature of these sections was highly sensitive to acetylcholine and adrenaline, and that the latter produced not relaxation but vigorous contraction. These formations failed completely to react to posterior-pituitary extract, even when subjected to concentrations of an ampoule solution of the order of $5 \times 10^{-3} - 1 \times 10^{-2}$. A few of the mounts from the walls of the large calibre ducts reacted by insignificant contractions (Fig. 22) to the highest concentrations, which were clearly above any physiological level. Unlike Levitskaya, however, Tverskoi did not notice any tendency for the musculature of the ducts to be relaxed under the influence of posterior-pituitary extract. One can assume that the differences in the results obtained by these authors are due to the properties of the objects being studied. Levitskaya was studying microscopic ducts which have the myoepithelial structures described by Richardson, whereas these elements are not known to exist in the walls of the large milk ducts and cistern on which Tverskoi experimented.

Thus the ducts, at any rate the large calibre ducts, and the cistern do not react to posterior-pituitary extract. If, therefore, one accepted the view of Ely and Petersen, one would be forced to the inescapable conclusion that the motor apparatus of the alveoli plays a unique role in milk ejection and that the musculature of the ducts and cistern has no part in this act. This conclusion is quite clearly seen to be untenable when we make a somewhat closer examination of the essence of the processes that occur in the motor apparatus of the udder at the moment of milk ejection.

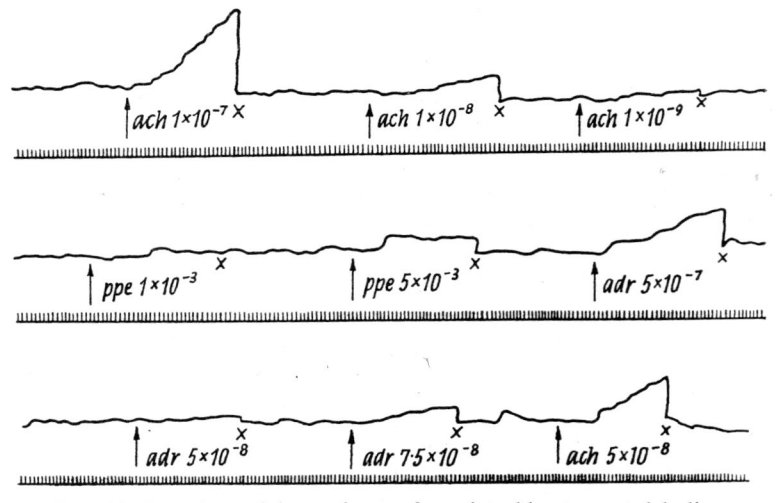

FIG. 22. Reaction of large ducts of cow's udder to acetylcholine (*ach*), adrenaline (*adr*) and ampoule solution of posterior-pituitary extract (*ppe*). (From Tverskoi, 1955b.)

Physiological description of the milk-ejection reflex. It has been shown that the skin zone of the teats and udder is the main receptory field of the milk-ejection reflex. It is important to note that the milk-ejection reflex arises immediately and simultaneously throughout the whole udder, whether all or only some of the teats are stimulated. This will, of course, only be true when milk ejection is freely effected, i.e., when the milk expelled from the alveoli does not encounter an insurmountable obstacle as a result of constriction of the ducts. Definite forms of the inhibition of milk ejection can be caused by closure or spasm of the sphincters at the mouths of the ducts which creates an obstacle to the passage of milk into the cistern. This does not, of course, exclude the possibility that this obstacle may exist to varying degrees in different quarters or even small lobes of the gland, in which case the discharge of milk into the cistern may commence at different times in the separate quarters and proceed at different rates. In some cases, especially in the incorrect conduct of machine milking, this circumstance may acquire great importance (Kobozev, 1953).

General milk ejection develops throughout the udder in goats when one teat is stimulated (Pavlov, cited by Baryshnikov *et al.*, 1951; Tsakhaev, 1953; Grachev, 1953) and when the other teat is drained with a catheter. Zaks and Tolbukhin (Zaks, 1955) have demonstrated that when as many as three teats of a cow are being drained and only one milked, milk is also yielded simultaneously throughout the udder. Under these conditions milk ejection is adequately effective even in those quarters of the udder that are not directly milked.

TABLE 2
THE YIELD OF SEPARATE QUARTERS OF THE UDDER WHEN MILKING ONE TEAT

Cow	Milking method	Milk yield (ml.) right quarters front	rear	left quarters front	rear
Ampula	Normal milking of all teats (A)	840	980	810	920
	Cannulation of 3 teats and milking of one (B)	850D	1140	880	1040
Gvozdika	A	2460	730	2600	1430
	B	2300D	760	2250	1380
Shpinatka 12	A	360	1580	830	1520
	B	380D	1560	800	1520
Zolotaya	A	1650	1080	1460	1730
	B	1500D	1080	1400	1690

Note: D indicates the quarter being milked.

Thus, in test milkings (see Table 2) there was hardly any difference between the yield from the control milkings and from milkings in which one teat was milked and the other three were catheterized. This holds both for cows in which the four quarters of the udder are evenly developed (Ampula, Zolotaya) and for those in which the quarters differ markedly (Gvozdika, Shpinatka 12). It can also be seen that the milked teat has no "advantages" over the catheterized teats.

Both the simultaneousness and the completeness of milk ejection throughout the udder when only one teat is stimulated are of definite practical significance. The fact that milk ejection is simultaneous clearly explains the decline in the yield and fat content of milk from the "subsequent" quarters when separate teats are milked in turn. This is well known to practical workers. The energy of milk ejection in the last quarter is considerably lowered before its turn comes. This is of significance for any method of hand milking in which pairs of teats are milked in turn. The negative significance of these factors is especially great when the quarters of the udder are unevenly developed. For this reason the best hand-milking methods will be those that ensure that the udder is emptied as evenly and simultaneously as possible; experience shows that milking is most effective when both halves of the udder are milked simultaneously by two milkmaids, but despite its physiological advantages this method can scarcely be of great practical importance, for quite understandable reasons. It is also certain that one of the advantages of machine milking is precisely that the separate quarters of the udder are milked simultaneously.

The question may arise as to whether this factor plays a significant role in the wild ancestors of the cow and also in domestic cows suckling calves, especially since there are no grounds for assuming that this feature in the milk-ejection reflex is a comparatively late acquisition of high-yielding cows. According to Martyugin (1944), a calf alternates between the four quarters of the udder in a single feed, but can scarcely evacuate all the quarters fully on one occasion, even in turn. It is probable that a calf comes to suckle more frequently than the number of times a cow is normally milked and that therefore the udder does not become particularly overfilled. M. A. Gofman has observed that the kid may go to the goat as many as 120 times a day in the days immediately after kidding and that this figure subsequently falls to 20–25.

The fact that unmilked quarters of the udder can be totally evacuated through a catheter when only one teat is milked is of importance when one or more teats are catheterized for veterinary reasons to empty the udder of milk.

In goats a unilateral reaction may also be obtained under certain conditions. When they applied the stimulus of a weak induction current to one teat, Baryshnikov and Pavlov (Baryshnikov et al., 1953) elicited the secretion of a certain quantity of milk only on the stimulated side (Fig. 23). It is most probable that in this case the flow of milk was not due to the reflex of the alveoli but to discharge of part of the milk from the ducts into the cistern, in the same way as in the intervals between milkings.

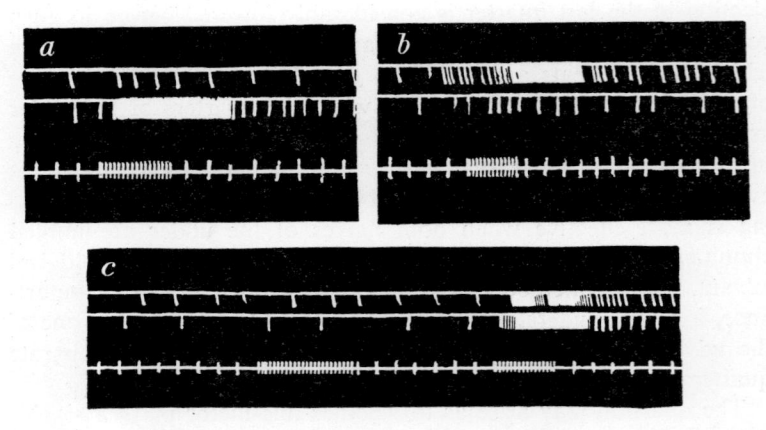

FIG. 23. Milk ejection reaction when skin at base of teats and udder is stimulated in goats. (From Baryshnikov et al., 1953.)

Reading from above: recording of drops of milk from right teat, from left teat, time scale 5 sec. Stimulation is shown by the closely spaced lines on the time scale: a—left teat; b—right teat; c (left)—udder; c (right)—left teat.

The skin of the teats is the most effective reflexogenic zone. G. N. Pavlov (see Bogdashev and Eliseev, 1951), who used an induction current as the stimulus, has shown on goats that the basal region of the teat is particularly reactive. Nevertheless, the full effect can be obtained by stimulation of other areas of the teat.

Considerably weaker effects occur when the skin of the udder is stimulated, and stimulation becomes less effective as one moves further from the teats. Baryshnikov and Pavlov (see Baryshnikov et al., 1953) noted that the milk-ejection reflex was absent when the skin of a goat's udder was stimulated with an induction current of a certain strength, but that the application of a stimulus of the same strength to the base of the teat caused milk ejection from both sides. A reaction of this kind is depicted in Fig. 23.

The morphological data of Bogdashev and Eliseev (1951) on "sensitivity zones" of the udder, which these authors established from the distribution of nerves in the skin of the teats and udder, are of interest in this respect.

It is still difficult to say with certainty which stimuli are most important in the production of complete milk ejection. If the act of normal hand milking is analysed from this point of view, the following main aspects can be distinguished:

1. *Tactile stimuli of the skin of the teats and udder.* These stimuli occur during udder massage, washing and milking. Since isolated tactile stimulation of the surface receptors of the udder is generally impossible in pure form, it could scarcely cause complete milk ejection with contraction of the alveoli. In any case, in our experiments on cows the use of stimuli in this form only led to the discharge of milk from the ducts into the cistern; it was only occasionally that complete milk ejection, including the discharge of the alveolar portion, was obtained in this manner.

2. *Stimulation of the deep receptors of the teat tissues when the teats are squeezed and stretched.* These stimuli are clearly the most effective—complete milk ejection occurs when the teats are milked and sham milking, when compression of the teat is not accompanied by the extraction of milk, is equally effective. One can suggest from Tsakhaev's data (1953), according to which the afferent fibres of milk ejection are contained in the dorsal columns of the spinal cord together with the conductors of muscular sensitivity, that the receptors of the deep tissues of the teat are in some degree similar to the proprioceptors of the skeletal muscles. But this question is in need of further study, since there has in general been little morphological or physiological study of the receptors of the smooth musculature and it is not at present easy to say how acceptable an anology between the reception of the skeletal and the smooth musculature can be.

3. *Stimulation of the receptors (pressoreceptors) of the mucous membrane of the teat system.* Excitation of these receptors during milking occurs when the milk is expressed by hand, especially when milking with the palm, which creates high pressure in the teat cistern. It is difficult to draw a distinction between stimuli of this category

and those described under Point 2. They are clearly also highly effective.

4. *Stimulation of the receptors of the teat canal when milk is expressed from the teat.* These stimuli are clearly not of decisive importance; as already stated, complete milk ejection can occur in sham milking, when milk is not milked out through the teat canals.

The frequency with which the teat receptors are stimulated is of basic importance for the efficacy of the unconditioned reflex of milk ejection. It has been empirically established that the best results in milking are obtained when the teat is squeezed 90–100 times a minute. This is the normal rate of qualified, well-trained milkers.

How does this correspond to the optimum working rhythm of the pulsator of the milking machine?

In the general practice of machine milking (we are quoting from Korolev, 1953) the pulsator is normally set at 40–50 pulsations a minute, i.e., each teat only receives approximately half the stimuli in a minute that it would receive from hand milking. But since machine milking differs from hand milking in that not two but four teats are stimulated simultaneously, the total number of specific impulses entering the central nervous system from the udder is approximately the same in hand and machine milking.

Practical experience is here fully confirmed by experimental analysis. Grachev (1953) established in experiments on goats that a similar rate of stimulation of the teat was closest to the physiological optimum. In his experiments one of the goat's teats was drained by a catheter and the teat of the second gland was stimulated after the cisternal portion (the "mechanical" portion in Grachev's terminology) had been completely drained through the catheter. Rates of stimulation between 12 and 240 stimuli a minute were tested in different experiments. The stimulus employed was hand pressure, as in milking. Rates of stimulation between 84 and 132 stimuli a minute were most effective. Under these conditions the latent period of the reflex was 30–35 sec., almost all (up to 96%) of the alveolar portion was extracted and additional stripping only yielded 3% of the milk of a single milking. When the frequency of stimulation was increased to 200–216 a minute, the latent period of the reflex was extended to 60–85 sec. and there was a marked decline in the efficacy of the reflex. With this rhythm only 40% of the alveolar milk was removed through the catheter and the remaining 60% had to be extracted by hand stripping after removal of the catheter. I am prompted to say that this result recalls what happens in ineffective machine milking, when a large part of the yield is obtained by hand stripping.

Reduction in the frequency of stimulation had quite similar results and the reflex disappeared entirely at frequencies of from 12–36 stimuli a minute.

It was also found that the limits of the optimum frequency vary in relation to the stage of the lactation, and that they are widest when the yield of the animal is at its highest and contract towards the close of the lactation. There was also a considerable extension in the optimum limits when the time of the next milking was put back or when one milking was omitted. Grachev associates this with an increase in the excitability of the "lactation centre". Grachev's facts are interpreted in the light of the general features of the optimum and pessimum frequency of stimulation established by Vvedenskii.

A certain minimum number of stimulations of the teat is required to bring about milk ejection. In goats (Tsakhaev's data) complete milk ejection normally develops after 10–15 compressions of the teat. Partial milk ejection, after which one can obtain a new reaction, develops when there are fewer stimulations (2–6). In this case milk ejection in the goat can be "fractionated" into three or four portions. This phenomenon needs further analysis. It is possible that what takes place is not true ejection, accompanied by contraction of the alveoli, but merely the partial passage of milk from the ducts into the cistern, similar to that observed by Baryshnikov and Pavlov when the skin of one of the teats was subjected to a weak induction current.

In cows a fully effective milk-ejection reflex could only be repeated some considerable time after it was first elicited. Zaks and Tolbukhin (Zaks, 1955) have demonstrated that 20 minutes after the milking of one half of the udder only milk present in the cistern can be milked out of the other half and alveolar milk is not discharged. The experiments were conducted with four cows during the daytime milking (at 4 o'clock). After normal preparation the right half of the udder was milked and this was followed after a fixed interval by milking of the left half. The yield of each quarter of the udder had first been established by milking into a pail with four compartments. It was found that there was no significant decline in the yield of the second half if the time between the milking of both halves did not exceed 10–15 min. Further increase of this interval invariably led to a considerable decline in the yield of the left side (Table 3).

TABLE 3
DECREASED YIELD OF LEFT HALF OF UDDER

Cow	Yield (ml.) normal milking	Yield (ml.) milking delayed 20 min.	Difference ml.	Difference %
Shkoda	4270	3610	660	15·4
Shpinatka 12	3790	2830	960	25·3
Shvedka	2485	1920	565	22·7
Neitral'naya	4205	2540	1665	39·5
Average	3687	2725	962	25·7

Thus, delay in milking leads to a considerable decline in the milk yielded by the "second" half. It is also important to add that the negative results of this experiment are not restricted to the one experimental milking, but also affect subsequent normal milking; two or three milkings are normally required before the yield from the left half of the udder regains normal proportions. In this respect the consequences of extended milking remind one of the effect that develops when part of the milk extracted is returned to the cisterns. To the best of my knowledge this important circumstance was unknown and was not therefore taken into consideration in many experiments by those authors (such as Garkavi, 1936) who used milking of the right and left half of the udder at different times as a method for studying the effect of the frequency of milking on milk yield.

The results of our experiments with extended milking lead us to question why complete milking out of the half of the udder that is milked second is prevented under these conditions. It would be natural to assume that the reason is connected with the impossibility of obtaining a fully effective milk ejection reflex 20 minutes after it was elicited throughout the udder by the milking of the right half. The truth of this hypothesis has been confirmed. The same general method was employed in its verification as in the main series of experiments. The difference was that immediately before the milking of the "second" half commenced catheters were inserted in both left cisterns and all the milk flowing freely through the catheter was drained off. After this the most energetic milking of these teats combined with massage only yielded insignificant amounts of milk that did not exceed in volume the normal discharge from the ducts. In a number of repeat experiments we only once observed fully effective alveolar milk ejection under these conditions (in the cow Neitral'naya). Thus these additional experiments made it possible to establish two important facts: (1) a fully effective reflex cannot normally be obtained in the alveoli 20 minutes after milking; (2) at this time the volume of milk not obtained is not in the cisternal section of the udder's storage system. It is possible that when milk enters an unevacuated cistern in milk ejection further discharge from the alveoli and ducts may be made difficult for purely physical reasons at a certain stage in the filling of the cistern and part of the milk may remain in the "upper storey" of the udder. This is the portion that we were unable to obtain by the second milking. In further experiments we discharged the cisterns of the left half of the udder, draining them through catheters, before beginning to milk the right half. We found that this averted the negative effect of extended milking; the total volumes of milk obtained from the left half of the udder by preliminary evacuation of the cisterns and by milking was exactly the same as the yield from this half of the udder in normal simultaneous milking of both halves. The results of these experiments cannot, however, exclude another interpretation; namely, that when the "first" half is milked all the milk passes into the cisterns. In the subsequent period, when the tone of the alveoli is lowered and there is still considerable pressure in the extended cistern, part of the milk can return retrogressively to the alveolar section of the storage system. We have already mentioned the existence of a similar phenomenon in goats.

In my opinion further detailed analysis of the reasons for the negative effect of extended milking of this type would be of considerable practical importance, but the main conclusion can already be drawn: the reflex to the alveoli is not immediately rehabilitated after it has been once obtained—this requires a considerable time. In any case my data show that even two hours after the previous milking a fully effective reflex to the alveoli, leading to the discharge of milk with a high fat content typical of the alveolar portion, can only normally be obtained by prolonged milking manipulations of the empty teats. It is true that in these experiments the entry of milk into the cistern from the ducts is observed. If milk is present in sufficient quantities in the ducts this reaction develops easily, especially in response to massage and thermal stimulations of the udder. But this effect should not be confused with the true reflex to the alveoli; in the conditions of this experiment both these reactions can be clearly distinguished from the amount of milk removed and especially from the extent of the latent period.

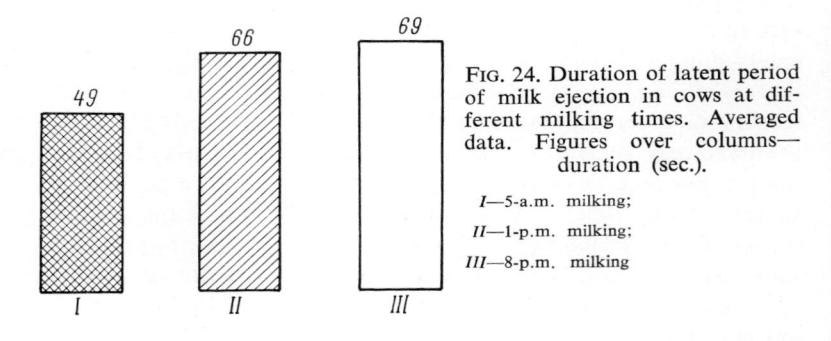

FIG. 24. Duration of latent period of milk ejection in cows at different milking times. Averaged data. Figures over columns—duration (sec.).

I—5-a.m. milking;
II—1-p.m. milking;
III—8-p.m. milking

It should be remembered that the extent of the latent period of the reflex to the posterior pituitary, which is associated with the secretion of oxytocin and the contraction of the alveoli, is subject to considerable variation in relation to the conditions under which the reflex is evoked. At milking time (when the storage system is comparatively full) the latent period of the reflex is 57 sec. on average. However, our observations (Zaks and Pavlov, 1952) of milkings at various hours of the day show that the duration of the latent period increases from 49 sec. on average at the morning milking to 69 sec. at the evening milking (Fig. 24). In similar experiments Syusyukin (1955) obtained results that exactly coincided with our own.

This relates only to milking at the normal times. When milking takes place at an unusual time, especially if it is soon after the previous milking, the latent period of the reflex to the alveoli is extended in the majority of cows to 3–6 min. The latent period of the reflex that affects the passage of milk from the ducts into the cistern is generally shorter (15–20 sec.) and rarely exceeds 40–60 sec. It is not so sharply dependent on the time of milking and the extent to which the storage system of the udder is filled.

This view of the slow restoration of the milk-ejection reflex is shared by many investigators (Ragsdale, Brody and Turner, 1924; Turner, 1935; Garrison and Turner, 1936), but is not universally accepted. An opposing view-point is held, for example, by Whittlestone (1951), who asserts that the cow can respond to additional stimuli applied immediately after milking "by the secretion of a second portion of the milk-ejection hormone". Whittlestone explains the mechanism of milk removal in hand stripping after machine milking in the same way.

In a later study Whittlestone et al. (1952) conducted a series of experiments on two cows with regular milking at 2-hourly intervals. They concluded that the total yield on test days coincided quite closely with the yield on control days when the animals were milked twice a day. There are some basic details in the work, however, which compel one to question the main conclusion of the authors that the capacity for fully effective milk ejection after short periods of time is a characteristic of dairy cows. First, cows of "good temperament" were specially selected for this experiment and, secondly, the result indicated by the authors was only obtained when all the conditions under which these cows were normally milked were strictly maintained. The slightest deviation from the normal pattern had a marked effect on the results of the milking.

Finally, these authors suggest that previous findings, that it was difficult or impossible to obtain fully effective milk ejection 2 hours after milking, were based on experiments in which constant conditions were not strictly maintained. But their own data undoubtedly show that it is more difficult to induce milk ejection after short periods than under normal conditions, inasmuch as they had to specially select suitable animals for the experiment and observe special conditions.

The stimuli operative on the receptor apparatus in normal milking are extremely diverse. In the main, however, they are all purely mechanical in nature and therefore only give rise to excitation in various groups of mechanoreceptors reached by the surface receptors of the skin of the teat, the receptors of its deep tissues and the interoceptors of the cistern, etc. It is, however, possible that purely mechanical stimuli do not exhaust the list of stimuli which can be of significance in milk removal. Thus, for example, the significance of temperature stimuli had not only not been studied, but had not even been raised until quite recently.* There are, moveover, definite biological reasons for its significance. After all, the act of milking, whether by hand or by machine, is in some measure called on to imitate the natural stimulus for the animal—the act of suckling. Examination of this act will certainly be of value both in relation to the purposes of our study and for perfecting milking technique.

In speaking of the possible significance of thermal stimuli in the act of milk ejection, one has to bear in mind that there are considerable temperature differences between the skin of the teats and the mouth of the calf.

We found from repeated measurements of the teat skin temperature that when the temperature in the cattle shed is 10–12°C., the temperature of the teats before milking commences is 29–31·5°C., whilst in the calf's mouth, between the tongue and the palate, it reaches 38°; there is reason to consider that with temperature differences of this order the thermal factor in suckling is quite an effective stimulus of certain receptors.

When studying a new method for increasing the fat content of milk by washing the udder with warm water before milking as suggested by K. M. Letsko, a milkmaid on the Suoyarvi state farm, Zaks, Egorova, Niukkanen and Olenov (1952) established that water heated to 53–56°C. and water vapour at a similar temperature had an undoubted effect on the motor apparatus of the udder when applied to the skin of the teats and udder, causing relaxation of the mouths of the ducts and thus facilitating removal of the final and most fatty portions of the milk. Olenov and Niukkanen (Egorova *et al.*, 1953) found that when the udder was warmed with water vapour after milking dry, but was not massaged, the amount of the final strippings in a certain temperature range increased in

---

* It is true that in enumerating the udder receptors that can be of significance in milk ejection, Petersen (1950) does mention thermoreceptors as well as tactile and pressor receptors, but the question is not considered in any detail.

proportion to the temperature employed to heat the vapour. These experiments showed that after complete hand milking the effect of high temperature alone, under conditions in which mechanical influence is excluded, causes an additional inflow of milk into the cistern. There is a clearly defined relationship between the strength of the thermal stimulus and the magnitude of the effect. Thus, in an experiment on 8 cows which had been milked "dry" the additional effect of heat caused 28 ml. to pass into the cistern when the water temperature was 30°, 53 ml. at 40° and 143 ml. at 56°C. These are averaged figures for 3 milkings of each cow in the group for each temperature. Even so, the feature was observed in all the animals in the experiments without exception.

The thermal reflex is primarily connected with the skin of the teats, since the isolated action of heat on the skin of the udder does not give rise to a similar effect. The thermal reflex is of a diffuse kind: the passage of milk into the cisterns in all quarters of the udder also occurs when only one teat is subjected to the thermal effect. In one series of experiments (on 4 cows), for example, the average strippings from the four quarters were 162 ml. when heat was applied to all the teats and 173 ml. when only the right fore teat was washed in hot water (Zaks, Olenov and Saltup, 1954).

Pavlov and Markaryan (1955) observed a considerable increase in the fat content of the milk when a small sack filled with heated sand was placed on the sacral region. It is still difficult to say whether this phenomenon is absolutely identical with the thermal reflex described by us, which was obtained from the skin of the teats and was primarily connected with the motor apparatus of the udder.

Fedii (1961) has discovered an unusual case of thermal influence on the fat content of milk. In cows with external anastomosis of the small intestine (Sineshchekov's method), artificial lowering of the temperature of the chyme in the intestine to +20°C. and especially to +15°C. caused a considerable increase in the percentage of fat in the milk without any decline in yield. It is as yet difficult to say what part the synthesis and secretion of fat play in this effect. Inasmuch, however, as there is a considerable after effect, there is clearly an intensification in synthesis.

The extent to which animals are capable of differentiating

qualitative and quantitative differences in mechanical and thermal unconditioned stimuli received by the receptor apparatus of the udder is of great importance.

Grachev (1953) combined an unconditioned food response with various types of stimulation to the skin of the teats and udder, which had previously had no effect on the working of the salivary gland. In this manner he was able to show precisely that a number of stimuli of the mammary gland could be differentiated. It was found, for example, that a differential response to the frequency with which the teat is squeezed can be produced fairly easily in goats; the limit of distinction is 60 and 40 compressions a minute. Differentiation of stimuli to the skin of the teats and that of the lower part of the udder develops most rapidly. As little as one or two juxtapositions sometimes suffice for this. At the same time, differentiation of stimuli to the skin of the symmetrical, right and left, halves of the udder was found to be extremely difficult and highly unstable. This is in full agreement with the facts which we have already given concerning the diffuse nature of the reflex of milk ejection.

Differentiation of stimuli when milking with the palm and with the fingers can be clearly and rapidly developed. For the thermal stimulus differentiation has been produced for temperatures of the order of 32–36°C. and 16–20°C. It is most desirable that studies of this type should be extended to cows, in order to obtain precise and detailed information on the degree to which these animals can differentiate between the various types of stimulus to which the udder is subjected in hand and machine milking. This "charting" of differentiations will be of great practical importance in the development of the most rational and effective milking procedures.

In conclusion, we should dwell on the possibility of obtaining reflexes to the motor apparatus of the udder from other, non-specific zones and also under the influence of non-specific stimuli.

In this connexion, impulses from the sexual sphere are of particular significance. Andersson (1951b) has established that mechanical stimulation of the vaginal section of the uterine cervix in goats causes milk ejection.*. Other facts also point to the

---

* The connexion between milk ejection and stimulation of the sexual organs has long been known and has even been used for practical purposes. In his *History* Herodotus gives an extremely picturesque description of a

existence of similar connexions between the mammary gland and the sexual organs. According to Pickles (1953) and Harris and Pickles (1953), coitus causes milk ejection in nursing mothers. It is difficult to explain these facts other than by the reflex secretion of oxytocic substances of the posterior pituitary when the corresponding receptors of the sexual organs are stimulated. It is also common knowledge that this connexion between the mammary gland and the sexual organs is two-way. It suffices to mention the well-known gynaecological fact that there are vigorous contractions of the uterus during breast feeding.

Andersson (1951b) discovered that milk ejection can be caused in goats by stimulation of the central end of the vagus. He explains this phenomenon by the existence of a reflex effect on afferent fibres of this nerve to the neurohypophysis, as a result of which substances with an oxytocic effect are secreted along with other hormones. This fact is of considerable interest and should certainly be painstakingly analysed. Stimulation of the central end of a transected vagus causes excitation of afferent fibres from the most diverse receptor zones, including fibres running from the oesophageal groove, with which the rumination reflex is known to be associated; the latter can also be obtained by stimulation of the central end of the vagus. If this is compared with the facts given above concerning the possibility of obtaining the rumination reflex from the udder (Grachev, Azimov), one may consider that, as in the case of the sexual organs, the connexion between the mammary gland and the digestive system is two-way.

Milk ejection as a two stage act. It was thought until quite recently that the force needed to cause the expulsion of milk at the moment of milk ejection, thus facilitating milking of the cow, was created by simultaneous contraction both of the alveolar myoepithelium and of the smooth musculature of the udder's storage system as a whole. This view has been firmly established since the studies of Ely and Petersen (1941) and has been repeated by many authors without revision. Nevertheless, we now have a great deal of factual

method sometimes employed by the Scythians to milk mares: "Milking is conducted in the following manner: they place bone tubes, very similar to flutes, in the sexual parts of the mares and blow down them; meanwhile, others milk the mares. They say that they do this because blowing the air swells the veins of the mare and the udder is lowered." (Retranslated from Russian edition of 1888, Vol. 1, Bk. 4.)

material to show that adaptive variations in the tone of the smooth musculature of the ducts and cistern in the act of milk ejection are immeasurably more complex than the simple overall contraction assumed by Ely and Petersen. The initial factual material which compelled us to consider the relaxation in the tone of the smooth musculature of the cistern before milk ejection was obtained from figures for 115 measurements of the maximum pressure of milk ejection in 11 cows (Zaks and Pavlov, 1952). Before milking commenced, the person conducting the experiment introduced a catheter into one of the cisterns and connected it with a manometer after the cisternal milk had been totally removed; the usual milkmaid was then called and began milking after the normal daily preparatory manipulations. The manometer readings were recorded visually in the process of milk ejection.

Before milking commenced pressure in the cistern of the catheterized teat was equal to zero. We noted a very distinctive feature in these experiments: when the milkmaid first touched the other teats, and sometimes even earlier when she approached, the milk in the manometer and connecting tubes began to move towards the cistern, as if affected by a suctional force. This was at first inexplicable since we were too accustomed to the idea that milking is necessarily and above all accompanied by an increase in pressure in the udder's storage system. Pressure subsequently began to rise and reached a definite maximum in 2 min on average; after this it settled down at a steady level and subsequently declined somewhat. After maximum pressure had been obtained the manometer was disconnected and the alveolar portion passed through the catheter and measured. Simple observation of fluctuations in the level of the milk in the manometer during milk ejection had already shown that the rise in pressure was not smooth and even, but stepped and intermittent, and that there could sometimes be periodic slight declines in pressure.

When graphs were constructed from the material we found a clearly defined relationship between the maximum pressure level of milk ejection and the volume of the alveolar portion of the milk. The curve that expresses this relationship is, however, extremely unusual. Pressure rises evenly up to a point corresponding to a pressure of 15 cm of milk on the y-axis and 400 g on the x-axis, and the curve is almost linear in this interval; it subsequently becomes markedly stepped and there are declines, although the general pattern is one of continued rise (Fig. 25). We assumed from the form of the curve that there is a certain decline in the tone of some sections of the storage system at the same time as it increases in other sections, and that this prevents excessive pressure rise. We did not, however, discover any clear relationship between the amount of alveolar milk extracted and the rate at which pressure attained its maximum. This rate is undoubtedly dependent on three variables: the extent to which the alveoli are filled, the energy with which milk is expelled from the alveoli into the cistern and the level of resistance created in the ducts. The latter should hinder the expulsion of milk and should therefore vary the rate at which pressure in the cistern, where we are measuring it, can reach its highest level. One would expect that the contractile energy of the

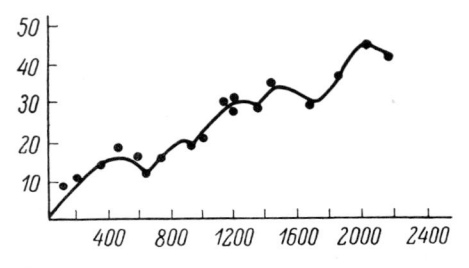

FIG. 25. Relationship between maximum pressure of milk ejection and size of the alveolar portion of the milk.

X-axis—alveolar portion (g.); y-axis—maximum pressure of milk ejection (cm. of milk).

alveoli would be to some extent determined by the extent to which they were filled, i.e. by the amount of alveolar milk, but the second variable—the level of resistance in the ducts—is apparently an even greater influence. In our experimental conditions the first quantity, i.e. the amount of alveolar milk, could be determined with accuracy. The second quantity—the resistance or tone of the ducts—could not, unfortunately, be directly assessed. Even these data however showed that the relationships between the reaction of the alveolar myoepithelium and the musculature of the ducts and cisterns is considerably more complex than was supposed by Ely and Petersen and a number of other authors.

The data obtained in this series of experiments were further studied by visual recording of variations in intracisternal pressure during the act of milk ejection (Zaks, 1955).

One can see from visual recording of intracisternal pressure during milking that the reaction of the motor apparatus of the udder does not begin with a rise in pressure, as was previously thought; on the contrary, pressure in the cistern falls at the commencement of milking and sometimes during milking. This is not always observed and varies in degree in relation to the initial fullness of the udder. When the udder is not very full or after it has been evacuated through a catheter at the commencement of milking, negative pressure may even occur in response to milking (Fig. 26). In certain

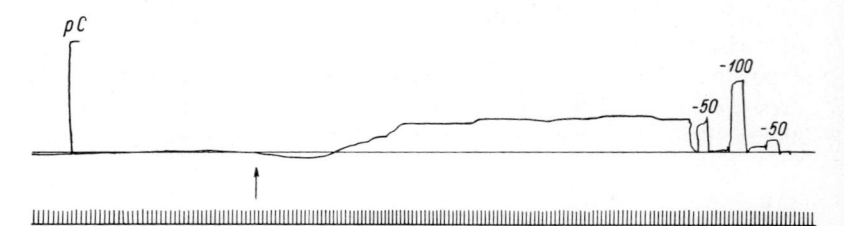

FIG. 26. Variations in intracisternal pressure on milking. Reading from above: recording of pressure in the cistern of the right front teat, zero pressure line, time scale 5 sec. pC—pressure in cistern before evacuation through cannula. Arrow—beginning of milking. Right—pressure variations in the cistern after partial draining of milk; figures—amount of milk discharged (g.).

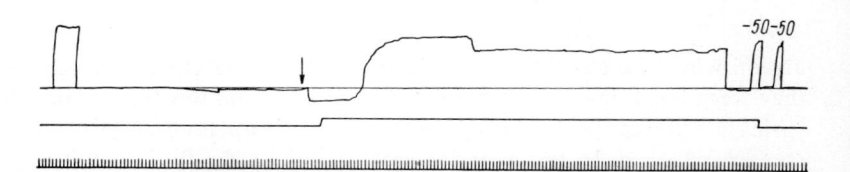

FIG. 27. Conditioned reflex variations in intracisternal pressure on milking. Reading from above: intracisternal pressure, zero pressure line, beginning and end of milking. Other symbols as in Fig. 26.

conditions this reaction may be observed before the commencement of milking in the preparation for it; it arises by conditioned reflex in response to the normal stimuli associated with milking: approach of the milkmaid, binding of the tail, etc. Thus this distinctive relaxation reflex may be induced by unconditioned and conditioned stimuli associated with milking (Fig. 27).

These data enable us to assert that the commencement of

milking is accompanied by reflex lowering of the tone of the musculature in the cistern. One can still not say exactly what changes are occurring in the tone of the ducts at this moment and what is happening to the pressure in their system, since we still do not have direct methods for determining these values. Nevertheless, as mentioned above (Borsuk and Zaks, 1955), exteroceptive stimuli of the teat and udder skin and the appropriate conditioned stimuli (Borsuk, 1955a) can cause the movement and discharge of milk from the ducts into the cisterns under these conditions. It follows, therefore, that a weakening in the tone of the cisterns is accompanied by a complex redistribution of the tone of the ducts, as a result of which milk is able to pass into the cisterns. It is highly probable that the sphincters of the ducts are relaxed at the same time as the tone of the musculature of their walls is enhanced. It is easy to see the physiological significance of these reflexes. They alter the tone of the cistern and ducts before the alveoli begin to contract and thus facilitate the movement of milk through the duct system and, in a sense, make space in the cistern for the milk which will be discharged into it from the alveolar section of the storage system in the next stage.

In the wild ancestors of present day high-yielding dairy cattle and when calves are reared at the teat this relaxation reflex probably served as a valve protecting the secretory tissue of the mammary gland from the harmful consequences of excessive pressure rise in the storage system of the udder, especially when the calf fails to empty all four quarters of the udder in a feed. We recall that milk ejection occurs in all four glands in the cow even if only one teat is stimulated. It is not therefore accidental that Gofman (1955) could not clearly detect this relaxation reflex in goats. She found that this first stage of milk ejection in goats is accompanied not by a decline but, on the contrary, by a slight increase in intramammary pressure, clearly associated with the influx (discharge) of certain amounts of milk from the ducts into the cistern. In the absence of simultaneous relaxation of the cistern this leads to a rise in pressure in its cavity. It is clear that the biological significance of the relaxation reflex is not so great for goats as for cows, since the former have a twin lobed udder and normally give birth to two or even three young.

Intracisternal pressure begins to increase in the next period of milk ejection, as can be seen from Fig. 26. This is due to contraction of the alveoli and influx of milk into the cisternal section. Nevertheless, either this increase in pressure is stepped or there is a decline in pressure after it has reached a certain maximum. This shows that lowering in the tone of the musculature of the storage system is not confined to the period before the alveoli begin to contract, but also occurs even during the forced evacuation of the alveoli. If pressure is recorded in an unmilked quarter one can see that the final pressure values are less in some cases than the initial value in the cistern before milking commences. If, after milking has finished, one lets out small portions of milk from the unmilked quarter pressure will be found to rise and not to fall in response to the discharge of 50–100 ml. Thus, when the cisternal section is filled and dilated the tone of its musculature is reflexly lowered, but is increased on evacuation and collapse. It may be considered that both the exteroceptors of the skin and the interoceptors of the storage system, the existence of which has been morphologically demonstrated by Krestinskaya (1952), take part in this reflex. The pressure on the walls of the storage system is the stimulus for these receptors.

It should be noticed that the increase in the tone of the cistern associated with the moment of its evacuation readily disappears if the base of the teat is very lightly massaged immediately after a small portion of milk has been drawn off and pressure has risen. It can be seen from Fig. 28 that pressure in the cistern then falls again and that the latent period of this reflex is dependent on the point at which the stimulus is applied. If the base of the same teat in which pressure is being measured is massaged 5–6 stimuli will produce the effect, but if another teat is massaged, the right rear teat for example, 26 stimuli are now needed to elicit a response. This is undoubtedly connected with irradiation of the excitation.

Our discovery of a lowering in intracisternal pressure has been confirmed by Nikitin *et al.* (1953) and Syusyukin (1955) in experiments in which pressure was not recorded but measured by a spring manometer, the dynamics of pressure variation being established from a curve constructed from the figures yielded by the experiment. Thus, data yielded by a completely different method are in full agreement with our own. In addition to contraction of the alveoli, reflex changes in the tone of the musculature of the cisterns and ducts are also involved in the complex reaction of the motor apparatus of the udder in response to milking. It can be assumed that these latter reflexes, unlike the reflex reaction of the alveoli, are effected by a purely nervous pathway, without the participation

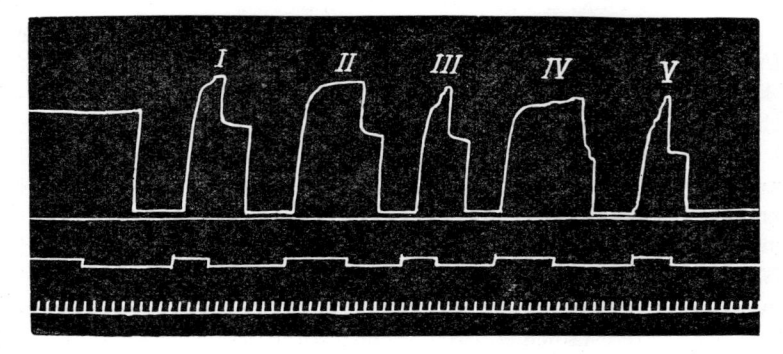

FIG. 28. Variations in pressure in the left front cistern after partial evacuation followed by massage of the base of the teat.

Reading from above: pressure variation when teats are massaged: *I*—left front 6 stimulations); *II*—left rear (26 stimulations); *III*—left front (6 stimulations); *IV*—right rear (20 stimulations); *V*—left front (6 stimulations); zero pressure line; record of commencement and termination of massage; time scale 5 sec.

of a humoral component. In support of this hypothesis it can be stated that these reflexes have a latent period that is short by comparison with that of the reflex reaction of the alveoli. In addition, the fact that reflexes of this type can be easily repeated, as is convincingly shown in Fig. 28, also distinguishes them markedly from the neurohumoral reflex concerned with contraction of the alveoli.

One can already base the concept of milk ejection as a complex two stage act on the foregoing facts. In the first stage there is a relaxation in the musculature of the cistern and a change in the tone of the ducts under the influence of conditioned and unconditioned stimuli associated with the preparation for and commencement of milking (approach of the milkmaid, clatter of the equipment, binding the tail, washing the udder, preliminary massage, etc.). At this stage the udder space and the ducts are, as it were, being prepared to pass and accept the milk which will be expelled from the alveoli in the following stage. The first stage is purely reflex; it is effected by direct efferent influences on the musculature of the udder. In the second stage, impulses that arise from milking manipulations reach the posterior pituitary, where they give rise to the secretion of oxytocin, which reaches the alveoli by a humoral pathway, where it causes contraction of the myoepithelium and the expulsion of milk; the second stage is thus neurohumoral.

There are other grounds in addition to the facts set out above for accepting this view. Mention should be made of the findings of Borsuk and Zaks (1955) on the mechanism by which milk is discharged into the cistern. This mechanism is clearly associated with a similar reaction of the ducts. Gofman (1955), who used visual recording to analyse milk removal and variation in intracisternal pressure in the act of milk ejection in goats, also concludes that milk ejection is a two stage act. Astrakhanskaya (1955) confirmed Gofman's findings and established that the first stage is not observed in goats on the denervated side of the udder in unilateral denervation, but is re-established after regeneration of the severed fibres. Pavlov (1955a) has shown that the first stage of milk ejection is retained in temporary cold block of a cross-section of the spinal cord, but that the second stage declines and is reestablished after removal of the block. In a chronic experiment a special thermophore through which water of known temperature could be circulated was established extradurally at the level of the boundary between the thoracic and lumbar sections of the spinal cord in a goat in such a manner that the ventral surface of the thermophore was against the upper (dorsal) columns of white matter. A cooled mixture of water and alcohol was passed through the thermophore until signs of the onset of a partial transverse block appeared in the form of disturbances to the motor functions of the rear limbs. The cisternal portion was then drained and when only occasional drops of milk were being discharged one teat was stimulated. Immediately afterwards milk was discharged from both teats; the distinctive features of this phenomenon are a short latent period, the insignificant total quantity of milk discharged and the fact that it can be reproduced after a relatively short time. This latter fact is a feature of the reflex. Olenov (1954) also noted that the reflex was rapidly restored in response to thermal stimulation of the udder. When the block was removed by passing water at 39°C. through the thermophore, it was possible to induce typical alveolar milk ejection, in which the latent period of the reflex is relatively long and in which considerable quantities of milk are discharged and the alveolar section is completely evacuated, by stimulation of the teat in imitation of milking. The differences between these two reflexes can be seen clearly in Fig. 29.

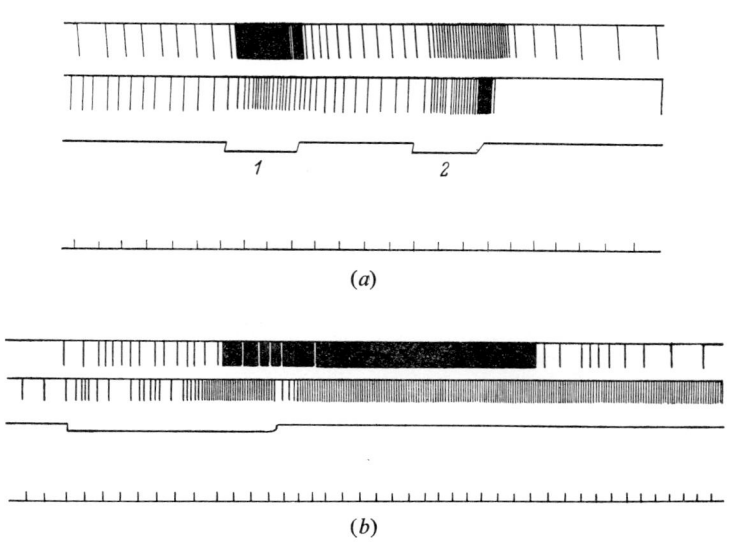

Fig. 29. Milk removal in a goat in response to stimulation of the teats: (a) with cold block of the dorsal area of the spinal cord, (b) after removal of the block. (From Pavlov, 1955a.).

Reading from above: recording of drops of milk from right teat, from left teat, indication of stimulus (*1*—right teat; *2*—left teat), time scale 5 sec.

The only "omission" in these workmanlike experiments was that there was no experiment in which the reflex of the first stage was studied when the spinal cord was blocked and when one half of the udder was totally denervated. A decline in the reaction of the first stage in the denervated half would have given absolute proof of the author's assertion that the reaction is segmental and that it occurs without the participation of the humoral link—the oxytocin of the posterior pituitary. In this particular the data of Astrakhanskaya and Pavlov might supplement each other and, taken together, eliminate the possible hypothesis that the first stage is an artifact. But Astrakhanskaya's data are not free from certain purely experimental defects: in her goats the existence of the first stage had not been established before transection of the nerves.

When analysing the mechanism of the thermal reflex I established a number of facts that reveal the special role of the reaction of the ducts in the act of milk ejection. It was established that the additional inflow of milk into the cistern when a thermal stimulus is applied to the teats is not connected with a reaction of the alveoli. The volume of milk that enters the cistern under these conditions bears little relation to the contents of the alveoli; thus, for example, this volume was 40–80 ml from one teat in each of three cows if heat was applied immediately after complete hand milking (without final massage) at the ordinary milking time, and approximately the same if heat was applied 2 hr after milking. The result was similar even although the alveoli had become partly filled by this time. This can be established easily by milking immediately after extraction of the thermal portion. Milking gave rise to typical milk ejection with the removal of 200–300 ml of milk from the same quarter of the udder from which the thermal reflex failed to produce more than 40–80 ml. The thermal reflex also differs from the reflex to the alveoli in the briefness of the latent period: in the experiment cited, additional discharge of milk from the alveoli only commenced after relatively prolonged (4–5 min) milking manipulations to the teats.

Although the basic concepts of milk ejection as a two stage act are based on the findings of Soviet investigators, Whittlestone (1950) arrives at an almost identical point of view. In an examination of Phillips' data he writes that "the milk ejection mechanism involves both a forcing of the milk from the alveoli and a decrease in the resistance of the ductules, due presumably to the shortening tendency caused by the contraction of the longitudinal myoepithelial cells shown by Richardson". (Quotation from Whittlestone, 1950). Espe (1946) also remarks that movement of the milk from the alveoli into the cistern may be facilitated by possible longitudinal contraction of the ducts at the moment of milk ejection.

New proofs of the existence of two stages in milk ejection have been obtained in our laboratory in analysis of the mechanism by which residual milk is removed from cows (Zaks and Olenov, 1955; Zaks, Olenov and Makeeva, 1956). It had earlier been assumed that the only reason for the movement of residual milk into the cistern was intensive contraction of the alveoli produced by the injection of a large dose of hormone, greatly in excess of the amount of oxytocin secreted under normal conditions in response to milking.

We began to doubt the correctness of this view after we found that in an experiment in which the residual milk was extracted in portions and not as a whole there were considerable variations in fat content in the first and subsequent portions. It was difficult to reconcile this fact with the generally accepted view that all the residual milk is present in the cisterns when one commences milking after injecting posterior-pituitary extract. It can be considered that both this view and the view that all the residual milk has the same fat content are exclusively based on data obtained by the normal procedure for extracting residual milk. The description of the standard procedure given by Koshi and Petersen (1955) is: (1) machine milking, (2) hand stripping, (3) injection of oxytocin, (4) hand milking of the residual milk after 10 min. It is assumed that the oxytocin will have been fully effective by this time and that all the residual milk which can be removed under these conditions will have passed into the cisterns. Very similar methods have been used by others who have studied residual milk.

We significantly altered the procedure. The right fore teat was catheterized and the cistern emptied of any milk it then contained. Next 5–6 ml of an ampoule solution of posterior-pituitary extract (approximately 30 i.u. of oxytocin) were injected subcutaneously.[1] A visual estimate was made of the time at which milk removal commenced and ended, and the milk was collected in small portions. When milk discharge had finished and the adjacent teats were stimulated by milking, massage and washing in water at 50–53°C., it was found that these stimuli invariably caused the flow of a variable additional amount of milk through the catheter. The reaction to posterior-pituitary extract normally commences 5–7 min after its injection and lasts for 7–10 min. Additional removal of milk in response to stimulation of the other teats commences after 50–70 sec and sometimes lasts 10–15 min, in relation to the amount of

[1] It has been specially established that the ultimate effect of identical doses of posterior-pituitary extract is approximately the same whether injected intravenously or subcutaneously; the only difference between the two methods is in the speed with which the response develops. We preferred subcutaneous injection, since most of the cows with which we were working could not be given intravenous injections unless they were immobilized.

TABLE 4

AMOUNT OF MILK (ML.) OBTAINED FROM THE RIGHT FRONT QUARTER BY THE INJECTION OF POSTERIOR-PITUITARY EXTRACT AND SUBSEQUENT MANIPULATIONS OF THE OTHER TEATS

Nature of influence	During milking	Immediately after milking	1 hour after milking
Posterior-pituitary extract	555·0	99·0	31·0
Manipulations of non-cannulated teats	220·0	73·0	212·0

milk and the nature of the stimuli. In a number of cases there was a vigorous discharge of a stream of milk; the discharge continues after the causal stimuli applied to the other teats have ceased. The experiments were conducted with 5 cows at milking time, immediately after the midday milking (12 o'clock) and 1 hr later, and each variant was tried on the same cows.

The averaged results of 15 experiments are shown in Table 4 and Fig. 30.

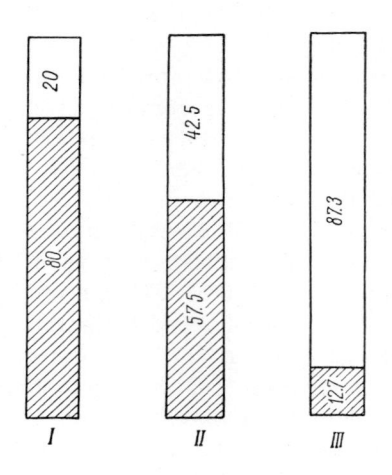

FIG. 30. Size of residual milk portions (as %) discharged after injection of posterior-pituitary extract (shaded area) and on subsequent manipulations of the teats (unshaded area).

I—before milking; *II*—immediately after milking; *III*—1 hr. after milking; all the residual milk extracted is treated as 100%.

We even obtained similar results in experiments in which the dose of posterior-pituitary extract was doubled and the injection repeated to eliminate the possible suggestion that our dosages were inadequate. The main conclusion to be drawn is that contraction of the alveoli brought about by posterior-pituitary extract is, in itself, not sufficient for complete expulsion of the residual milk into the cisterns. The force developed by the alveolar myoepithelium has to be combined with reflex alteration in the tone of the ducts.

These findings are a new and extremely fundamental proof of the two-stage nature of milk ejection. In this experiment the first and second stages seem to change places; the reaction of the alveoli due to the injection of the hormone is followed by reflex change in the tone of the smooth musculature of the ducts. But contraction of the alveoli is not sufficiently effective if it is due to a purely humoral agent, exogenous oxytocin, and if it occurs without preliminary reflex preparation of the ducts and cisterns. The force developed by the alveolar myoepithelium will cause movement of milk within the duct system and its transfer into the cisterns as long as the tension and pressure in the cavities of the alveoli overcome the resistance due to the tone of the ducts. Further entry of milk into the cisterns will cease when the expulsive force of the alveoli is equal to the resistance of the ducts. Flow into the cisterns will only recommence after the requisite reflex stimuli have lowered the resistance of the duct system that conducts the milk. When our predecessors milked out residual milk after injecting posterior-pituitary extract they were in fact dealing with two influences: a humoral influence on the alveoli and a reflex influence on the ducts. There was insufficient basis for ascribing the effect to the humoral influence alone, as was done.

From this point of view, differences in the results due to the time at which the experiments are conducted are of fundamental interest.

It can be seen from Fig. 30 that the (relative) effect of posterior-pituitary extract is greatest before milking, when the udder is full of milk. This is probably connected with the fact that there is a physiological lowering in the tone of the ducts at this time and their resistance can be overcome with less difficulty.

Posterior-pituitary extract has least effect 1 hr after milking; there is reason to believe that the tone and resistance of the ducts are at their highest at this time. It is, of course, possible that the varying effect of posterior-pituitary extract is dependent on the fullness of the alveoli. This alone cannot, however, explain the differences in the effectiveness of posterior-pituitary extract since its effect is still higher after milking, when the alveoli are least full and consequently least distended, than an hour later, when they have refilled to a certain extent. Consequently the effectiveness of the hormone is far more dependent on the tone and resistance in the system of ducts that carry the milk than on the extent alone to which the alveoli are distended. Nevertheless one can not exclude the possibility that the reactivity of the myoepithelium to oxytocin can vary at different times after milking. This possibility is the least probable when one bears in mind that our dosages were greatly in excess of threshold doses.

The concept of milk ejection as a two stage act provides a new approach to an explanation of the mechanisms by which milk ejection is inhibited. The rate of milk ejection and its effectiveness, i.e. the extent to which the storage system of the udder is evacuated, depend in the last analysis on the extent to which the overall resistance of the system that carries the milk is lowered in the first stage by adaptive changes in the tone of the musculature of the ducts and cisterns, and on the energy developed by the alveolar myoepithelium (i.e. on the extent of its contractions) in the second stage. Consequently, partial or total suppression of milk ejection always occurs when either the first or the second stage in the reaction, or both, are disturbed.

It is certain that many cases of disturbance in milk ejection are associated with the first stage. In his remarks on a paper by Dr. Mironov, I. P. Pavlov (1951) pointed out that the influences that normally inhibit milk removal lose a great deal of their effectiveness when the udder in denervated. This comment was made nearly sixty years ago, when it would, of course, have been impossible to distinguish between nervous and neurohumoral factors in milk removal. Nevertheless, the fact to which Pavlov drew attention is capable of only one interpretation in the light of contemporary data: if an inhibitory effect declines after denervation of the udder this means that this effect was associated with the efferent nervous pathways that reach the organ.

This hypothesis has been fully confirmed in subsequent work by Soviet investigators.

It has been established for sheep and goats by Zaks and E. F. Pavlov (Zaks, 1951) and for guinea pigs by Baryshnikov and G. N. Pavlov (Baryshnikov et al., 1951) that stimulation of the peripheral end of the external spermatic nerve that runs into the udder suppresses the removal of milk through a catheter for varying lengths of time.

G. N. Pavlov (Baryshnikov *et al.*, 1953) later analysed this phenomenon in chronic experiments on goats, in which the external spermatic nerve was stimulated by buried electrodes implanted on it. It was found that stimulation of the peripheral end of the transected nerve caused the removal of milk to cease on the side stimulated if there was slow discharge of milk into the cisterns not related to milk ejection (Fig. 31). If the nerve was stimulated when there was full milk ejection induced by reflex milking of the opposite teat, it seemed to terminate milk ejection on the side stimulated. Finally, a very complex effect developed when the unsevered nerve was stimulated. It has already been indicated that the stimulation of afferent fibres leads to reflex biphasic milk ejection, whilst simultaneous stimulation of the efferent fibres of this nerve causes a marked inhibition in milk ejection on the side of the stimulus, delaying it and reducing its intensity (Fig. 32). As in the experiments of Zaks and E. F. Pavlov, stimulation was always accompanied by loss of colour in the udder on that side and by retraction and shortening of the teat. This latter effect is clearly also an expression of a contractile reaction of the smooth musculature in response to stimulation of the efferent fibres of the nerve.

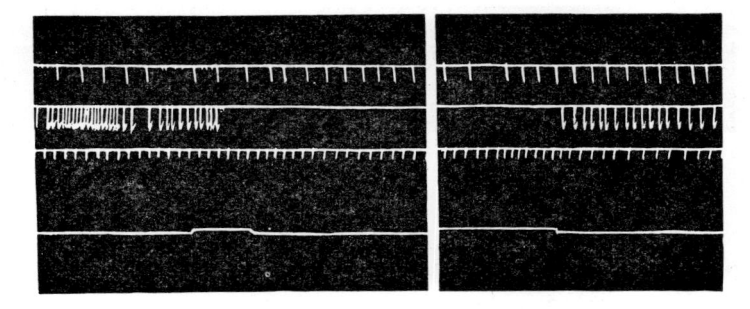

FIG. 31. The effect of stimulating the peripheral end of the left spermatic nerve of a goat on milk removal. (From Baryshnikov *et al.*, 1953.)

Reading from above: drops of milk from right teat, drops of milk from left teat, time scale 5 sec., indication of stimulation. Only part of curve shown: time interval of retention of drops of milk from the left—5 min.

Many aspects of this phenomenon are, of course, still not clear. It is probable that the very mechanism by which an impediment to the outflow of milk develops is similar to that observed by Zotikova and Levitskaya in the mammary gland of a mouse, in which annular constrictions of the ducts, that totally blocked their lumen, developed under the influence of adrenaline and when the nerve was stimulated. We have already suggested above that a similar role may be played in the udder of the cow by the annular muscles of the mouths of the ducts, described by Bogdashev and Eliseev.

What, however, is the mechanism by which these formations are relaxed and milk ejection facilitated? Is this relaxation effected as a result of inhibition in the corresponding spinal centres or is it associated with the existence of special relaxing fibres that lower the tone of the musculature?

In view of the fact that the various fibres are not simultaneously regenerated I have attempted, in joint experiments with E. F. Pavlov, to separate the stimulating and inhibiting effects of the different fibres in the trunk of the external spermatic nerve in sheep and goats by stimulating the nerve at various periods after transection. We were, however, only able to establish that the effect by which tone

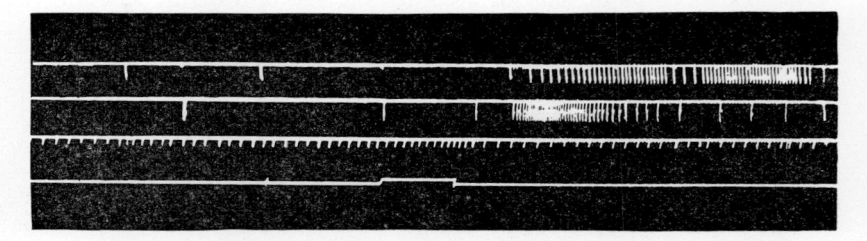

FIG. 32. Milk ejection when the intact right spermatic nerve of a goat is stimulated. (From Baryshnikov *et al.*, 1953.) Explanations as in Fig. 31.

is created in the musculature declines earlier than the vasoconstrictor effect. We were not able to separate effects on the musculature. These experiments cannot, of course, finally exclude the possibility that there are special relaxing fibres. It is possible that our observations were negative because the relaxing fibres are regenerated even before those responsible for the creation of tone. The question needs further study.

The facts here described provide a real basis for reconsidering the views of Ely and Petersen (1941), according to whom inhibition of milk ejection is associated with relaxation in the musculature of the ducts. These authors explained the inhibitory effect of adrenaline on milk ejection, which they had observed, by saying that this hormone relaxes the musculature of the cistern and ducts as if causing their paralysis. In this case Ely and Petersen assumed by analogy that adrenaline had a similar relaxing effect on the smooth musculature of the udder as on the musculature of the intestine, the bronchi and a number of other organs. Analogy, however, is not always a fruitful approach in physiology. We have already cited experiments which show that the effect of adrenaline on the musculature of the mammary gland is the opposite of that assumed by Ely and Petersen. This is shown, above all, by Tverskoi's direct experiments on isolated strips of udder musculature and by the microscopic observations of Levitskaya and Zotikova on the living animal, who have shown that adrenaline does not relax but causes an intensive contractile reaction in the smooth muscles of the ducts. It follows that the fact of the suppression of milk ejection under the influence of adrenaline, which was correctly noted by Ely and Petersen, was incorrectly explained. It is worthwhile dwelling on this since the incorrect view that the "paralytic" action of adrenaline on the smooth musculature of the udder is the reason for the retention of milk is quite widely held. It is maintained, in particular, by Espe (1946), who quotes Hammond (1936) and Turner (1933). Whittlestone (1954c) is of a similar opinion although it is true that his view of the antagonism between oxytocin and adrenaline is somewhat more complex. He considers that in addition to its paralysing influence (according to Ely and Petersen) on the smooth musculature, adrenaline contracts the blood vessels of the alveoli and slows down the intake of oxytocin to the myoepithelium. These considerations appear to find some confirmation in the data of Linzell (1954), according to whom the vessels of the mammary gland are especially sensitive to adrenaline. When the mammary gland was perfused, the blood of the donor had a marked vasoconstrictor effect in the mammary gland, which was completely eliminated if both splanchnic nerves were transected before bleeding or if adrenal medullectomy was performed. In Whittlestone's opinion these effects of adrenaline are also aggravated because adrenaline is more slowly destroyed within the organism than oxytocin. It is as yet difficult to say how significant these two latter factors—effect on the vessels and slow destruction—indicated by Whittlestone may be, but it is certain that there is insufficient basis for ascribing a paralytic action of adrenaline on the smooth musculature of the ducts to the latter. Although adrenaline inhibits milk ejection, it does so not as a result of paralysis but, on the contrary, as a result of spasm of the smooth musculature. In this respect its effect is similar to the action of the efferent (evidently adrenergic) nerves of the udder, stimulation of which, as already mentioned, gives rise to a similar effect. It is also certain that adrenaline plays a fundamental role in the cases of inhibition of milk ejection that so often occur when the animal is emotionally disturbed. It is this mechanism which evidently underlies the facts established by Cross (1955a), who observed a decline in the normal reaction of the mammary gland to injected oxytocin when the hyopthalamus of rabbits was stimulated by an electric current in the region of the paraventricular nucleus. A similar effect is produced by the injection of adrenaline, stimulation of the splanchnic nerves and stimulation of the sympathetic nerves of the mammary gland. Adrenalectomy abolishes the effect of stimulating the paraventricular nucleus. Cross explains all these phenomena by activation of the sympathetico-adrenal system in response to stimulation of its higher, hypothalamic centre.

It would certainly be quite incorrect to consider that all cases of the inhibition of milk ejection can be reduced to spastic changes in the tone of the ducts due to the influence of efferent nervous impulses or to adrenaline secreted by the animal in certain states.

Dyusembin (1957) has established in goats that sharp sound stimuli and stimulation of the skin with an electric current suppress the movement of milk into the cistern between milkings and inhibit the milk-ejection reflex. Inhibition of the first reaction is effected in the main by direct influences along the efferent nerves; the role of adrenaline is here only subsidiary. Suppression of the secretion of oxytocin, clearly associated with the mechanism established by Popovich, evidently plays a part together with effector nervous influences and adrenaline in the inhibition of milk ejection.

In a number of cases disturbance of milk ejection is associated with its second stage, by inhibition of the reflex to the neurohypophysis controlling the release of oxytocin. In milking practice one often encounters suppression of milk ejection in the second stage. This is shown by inability to obtain the alveolar milk which contains the highest percentage of fat. This type of phenomenon is most frequently encountered when the period between milkings is excessively reduced, or when milkmaids are changed or correct milking procedure is otherwise interfered with. Nevertheless there has still been no detailed physiological analysis of this important phenomenon. One important feature of this analysis should be a study of the dynamics of oxytocin entry into the blood stream, for which one would have to develop suitable rapid methods for testing this hormone in the blood. This is one problem for subsequent research. In the light of Dodd's previously mentioned findings that the oxytocin content of the neurohypophysis remains fairly constant and is not greatly altered after milking, it is clear that determination of oxytocic activity in the neurohypophysis itself will not be of particular significance in clarifying this question.

The role of direct mechanical influences on the udder in milk removal. There is now reason to consider that the reflex and reflex-humoral factors described above are supplemented in milk ejection by various subsidiary peripheral mechanisms, the importance of which had not previously been taken into consideration, or, more precisely, was totally unrealised. Cross (1954) showed in experiments on rabbits that mechanical stimulation (tapping with the handle of a scalpel) of the skin around the teat caused a brief rise in pressure in the ducts of the gland affected. Pressure reached 10 cm of water and stayed at this level for approximately 1 min. The form of this effect is strikingly reminiscent of the effect of intravenous injection of a small dose of oxytocin. Successive mechanical stimuli by tapping every 10 sec gave rise to a distinctive tetanus which was the summation of the effect. If a mechanical stimulus is combined with the injection of a small dose of oxytocin the magnitude of their effects is also summed. The most important factor is, however, that reaction to a mechanical stimulus is retained even after the establishment of a procaine block or transection of the nerves of the gland.

Cross considers that the fact discovered by him is an expression of the ability of the myoepithelium to react to direct mechanical stimuli. This supposition is highly probable in the light of the fact that both the elements responsible for contraction of the capillaries and the smooth musculature possess similar properties.

We obtained similar facts from a different form of the experiment on a different subject—the goat. The features of the removal of residual milk were studied in two goats in which the right half of the udder had been totally denervated. The experiments were conducted at the normal hours for morning milking. The denervated and the normal half of the udder were first milked dry simultaneously, after which measures were undertaken to expel all the residual milk. In one experimental variant both glands were first simultaneously massaged energetically and milked and the animal was given a subcutaneous injection of 1 ml of posterior-pituitary extract. Seven minutes later the goat was once again fully milked and this was followed by further deep massage of both halves of the udder and subsequent remilking (Table 5).

The only difference in the second variant was that the first massage was omitted and the following order was observed in the manipulations: (1) milking of both halves, (2) posterior-pituitary extract and milking, (3) massage and milking (Table 6).

TABLE 5
REMOVAL OF RESIDUAL MILK IN GOATS (IN ML.)
(FIRST VARIANT)

Goat	Left gland (normal)				Right gland (denervated)			
	milking	1st massage	posterior-pituitary extract	2nd massage	milking	1st massage	posterior-pituitary extract	2nd massage
Lipa	409·0	16·2	8·5	9·0	424·0	23·8	11·0	9·0
Marta	596·0	19·4	31·6	21·4	559·0	16·4	24·2	15·0

TABLE 6
REMOVAL OF RESIDUAL MILK IN GOATS (IN ML.)
(SECOND VARIANT)

Goat	Left gland (normal)			Right gland (denervated)		
	milking	posterior-pituitary extract	massage	milking	posterior-pituitary extract	massage
Lipa	418·0	18·6	8·5	388·5	12·5	11·3
Marta	533·0	20·3	33·5	493·5	25·4	42·0

Analysis of the figures in Tables 5 and 6 leads to the conclusion that in the first variant considerably more milk is obtained from the goats by massage than is expelled under the influence of posterior-pituitary extract; in the second variant the "massage" portion is also greater than the "injection" portion in one goat but slightly less in the other. These results are in general agreement with our data for an analysis of the humoral and reflex mechanisms responsible for the removal of residual milk in cows. The experiments on goats reveal a new fact however: that the capacity of the gland to yield residual milk under the influence of posterior-pituitary extract and, most important, under the influence of massage is not fundamentally affected after its denervation.

It had previously been held that massage had a reflex effect on the motor apparatus of the udder. It was thought that massage either caused reflex discharge of oxytocin from the posterior pituitary or a reflex reaction in the musculature of the ducts. In this respect there is little difference between reflexes to the mammary gland due to massage and the reaction associated, for example, with the thermal reflex. The data just cited in no way call in question the assumption that the effect of udder massage is of a reflex character; this assumption remains completely justified. Nevertheless, the fact that the effect of massage may be retained even when the connexions of the gland with the central nervous system are interrupted compels one to consider that some other mechanism which replaces the reflex mechanism is here involved in the evacuation of the alveoli. One cannot, of course, exclude the possibility that part of the milk, especially that present in ducts of large and medium calibre, may be purely mechanically forced into the cistern if massage is sufficiently vigorous. In view of the structural features of the udder it is unlikely that any considerable amount of milk would be obtained from the alveoli in this manner; to do so would require considerably greater force than is normally employed in udder massage. Complete expulsion of the residual milk is scarcely possible without the active participation of the most contractile elements of the alveoli.

It is clear that in denervation evacuation of the alveoli is associated with contraction of the myoepithelium in response to direct mechanical stimuli, as in Cross' experiments.

This is an entirely new question which is of fundamental theoretical and practical significance. It provides an explanation of the significance of the powerful mechanical influences to which the mammary glands of all mammals are subjected in the act of suckling the young. Anyone who has observed the act of suckling in goats, sheep, cows, pigs, rabbits, dogs and other animals will recall that in addition to the movements of the mouth and tongue that are intimately associated with the suckling of the milk, the young also make rhythmic and quite energetic thrusting movements with the head or paws. It is evident that in addition to tactile and thermal stimuli, which have a purely reflex effect, additional mechanical stimulation of the gland causes further contraction of the alveoli which combines with the effect of oxytocin in ensuring that the milk is drained as completely as possible, and may even replace oxytocin under certain conditions. A detailed study of this aspect of suckling is of great importance to milking technique and, in particular, to the technique of massage and the design of apparatus for mechanical massage of the udder.

Before concluding this section I must give some information on the properties of the teat sphincter. This is, unfortunately, the least studied part of the motor apparatus of the udder. Here our data are mainly confined to purely empirical observations. One can scarcely agree with Espe that "no one has ever reported feeling a marked easing up of the teat sphincter when the cow begins to 'let down' her milk." It is certain that the milkmaid can perceive a considerable lowering in the tone of the sphincter in many cows even earlier, when still milking the cisternal milk. According to Emerson (1929) there is a considerable lowering in the tone of the sphincter when the inguinal nerve is anaesthetized with a 2% solution of apothesine.

According to Tverskoi (1955b) isolated preparations of the musculature of the teat sphincter and strips from the walls of the large calibre ducts show a capacity for spontaneous rhythmic contractions which has not been found in similar preparations from the cistern. Further detailed study of the regulation of the sphincter function is of particular importance for further improvements in machine milking and especially for handling cows that are difficult to milk.

Conditioned reflexes of milk ejection. Conditioned reflex stimuli are also of importance in the act of milking. We have already given isolated examples of conditioned reflex influences on these processes in our general account of the processes by which milk is accumulated and ejected.

In ordinary milking all the circumstances that precede and accompany it and that are continually reinforced by the unconditioned stimuli of milking become of importance as a signal; this leads to the creation of a persistent stereotype in milking cows, especially on farms where milking procedure is fairly punctual. If certain elements in this stereotype are infringed, this may affect the efficiency of milking.

Here is an example from a paper by Grachev (1953). The goat in the experiment is milked in a stall in a special room, to which it is taken by the same milkmaid to whom it is accustomed. The milkmaid is not present at one of the experiments and the goat is taken and placed in the stall by a new person. The goat shows signs of being disturbed. The usual milkmaid then comes to milk the goat, but the animal does not see her, since its head is screened. Although all the milking techniques (unconditioned stimuli) are the same as those normally employed by this milkmaid, the results show that there has been a marked decline in the efficiency of milk ejection: the amount of milk obtained falls by 20–30%. In this case a change in the accustomed stereotype has had a quite marked negative effect on the unconditioned reflex. It is clear that the conditioned reflex component plays an extremely fundamental role in normal milking.

The relationships between the conditioned and unconditioned stimuli that induce milk ejection under normal farming conditions have been studied in our laboratory (Olenov and Zaks, 1956).

The first series of experiments were conducted with five cows handled by the milkmaid R. on the school farm of the Petrozavodsk agricultural high school. R.'s normal milking methods were first exactly timed and studied in every detail. R. milked with the palm, with an even rate of approximately 100 compressions of the teat a minute; she also milked the quarters of the udder in the correct order, taking the forequarters first and the rear quarters last. R.'s normal milking methods can therefore be said to be optimum in respect of the quality and strength of the unconditioned stimuli of the milk-ejection reflex.

The experiment consisted of introducing changes that worsened

R.'s normal milking technique into one of the daily milkings. These changes were as follows:

(1) slowing down the rate of milking—reducing the number of times the teat was squeezed in one minute from 100 to 60;

(2) instead of the normal order of milking (direct method) each quarter of the udder was milked in turn;

(3) instead of milking with the palm, milking was conducted by "plucking" with the fingers.

These faults in procedure were introduced together or separately on different days during the experiment and the results (yield, percentage of fat and total fat content) were compared with those of the previous day for the same milking, when the cow had been milked by the normal optimum methods. In what follows we shall refer to the simultaneous introduction of all three faults in procedure as "pessimum" milking. The experimental results are given in Table 7 (averaged data for the group).

TABLE 7

THE EFFECT OF CONDITIONED AND UNCONDITIONED MILKING STIMULI ON THE EFFICACY OF MILK EJECTION AMONG COWS MILKED BY R
(AVERAGED DATA FOR ONE COW)

Index	Control days (best milking)			Experimental days (milking procedure disturbed)		
	1st	2nd	3rd	1st*	2nd**	3rd***
Yield (l.)	3·14	3·05	3·09	3·27	2·98	3·18
Fat (%)	3·54	3·85	4·05	3·53	4·17	3·59
Output of milk fat (g.)	111·4	117·6	125·3	115·5	124·3	114·4
Output of milk fat on experimental days (as a % of output on control days	100·0	100·0	100·0	103·7	105·5	91·3

Note: One star in the "Experimental days" column indicates that the teat was squeezed 60 times per minute, two stars that each quarter of the udder was milked dry in turn, three stars that pessimum milking was employed. The numbering of the experimental days corresponds to that of the control days.

It should be noted that in all variations in the unconditioned stimuli we took every possible precaution not to affect those elements in the situation preceding and accompanying milking to which the cow was accustomed. There were also no variations in feeding throughout the period of the experiments.

The conclusion to be drawn from Table 7 may at first sight seem unexpected: the total output of milk fat did not decline when a method that clearly worsened milking conditions was used for the first time. Even such marked faults as a reduction in the rate of milking or successive milking of the quarters of the udder failed to have any fundamental effect on the result when applied separately and there was probably even a slight increase in the fat output. It was only when both procedures were introduced simultaneously and combined with milking by "plucking" that there was some decline in the fat output exclusively due to a decline in the percentage of fat by comparison with the previous control day. This circumstance is worthy of emphasis since the percentage of fat in the same milking on different days is normally subject to considerable variation. Attention should also be drawn to another circumstance that was eliminated in arriving at the averaged figures: the decline due to the simultaneous use of pessium milking methods was only found in three out of the five cows. Thus, the efficiency of milk ejection in cows from R.'s group was extremely stable despite the introduction of considerable variations in unconditioned stimuli. It should be remembered that we tried not to alter the elements of the normal pattern associated with milking (the time of milking of each cow, preliminary preparation, etc.).

How can this result be explained?

R. had looked after the cows since their first calving, and all except one had calved more than three times. We quite naturally assumed that milk ejection remained fully effective, despite the considerable variations in the unconditioned stimuli, owing to the conditioned reflex components of the reaction. During the years in which R. had worked with these cows temporary connexions had become firmly established, both owing to the frequency with which the patterns were repeated and, to an equal extent, to the highly effective nature and strength of the reinforcements.

We used seven cows that had had one calf from the "Vilga" farm of the Zaitsev state farm (Petrozavodsk) and which had recently been brought to the farm but had not previously been used for physiological research, to find out whether the frequency of reinforcement was, in fact, of importance. These cows were tended by T., who received them shortly (approximately 1 month) before the experiments started. T. was equally as efficient as a milkmaid as R.: she milked with the palm, observing the correct milking sequence (direct method), and squeezed the teat 100–120 times a minute. Thus, the main difference between the animals tended by R. and T. was merely that the latter's cows would not have been able to form such stable temporary connexions. It could be assumed that the sudden introduction of pessimum milking methods with these animals would worsen the result of milking, since milk ejection would not be maintained in this case by firmly established temporary connexions.

This hypothesis was verified by carrying out experiments similar to those just described, on the cows in T.'s group. We give an example of one of the experiments, in which pessimum milking methods were suddenly applied (Table 8).

The initial hypothesis was thus confirmed. The production of milk fat fell by 18·6% when pessimum milking was suddenly introduced. This was due both to a fall in yield and to simultaneous decline in the fat content of the milk. This experiment also revealed considerable individual differences in the reaction of the cows to pessimum milking. In one cow, for example, the decline in the output of milk fat reached 29%, whilst another failed to react in any way to the worsening in milking methods. It may be considered

TABLE 8
THE EFFECT OF PESSIMUM MILKING DURING THE DAY ON COWS MILKED BY T
(AVERAGED DATA)

Index	Control day (best milking)	Experimental day (pessimum milking)
Yield (l.)	2·78	2·36
Fat (%)	4·11	3·95
Output of milk fat (g.)	114·2	93·3
Output of milk fat on experimental day (as a % of output on control day)	100	81·4

that in her month of work with the new cows T. had already gone a fair way towards developing and consolidating conditioned reflexes, although to a different degree with different cows, and that if the experiment had been commenced somewhat earlier the result might have been even more significant. Even the results obtained, however, show that the complex of conditioned stimuli associated with milking is of great importance: if the temporary connexions are sufficiently established they can ensure that milk ejection will be highly effective, even when there is a considerable weakening in unconditioned stimuli. This is a further confirmation of the whole significance of the most punctilious uniformity in the way in which a milkmaid organises and arranges her work with her cows: taken in conjunction with correct strong unconditioned stimuli uniform milking conditions ensure that milk ejection will be as effective as possible.

TABLE 9

THE EFFECT OF VARIATIONS IN THE QUALITY OF UNCONDITIONED STIMULI ON THE EFFICACY OF MILK EJECTION AMONG COWS MILKED BY P
(AVERAGED DATA)

Index	Control days (customary milking procedure of milker P)		Experimental days (milking procedure modified)	
	1st	2nd	1st*	2nd**
Yield (l.)	3·04	3·08	3·15	2·93
Fat (%)	3·44	3·69	3·80	3·18
Output of milk fat (g.)	104·9	113·0	119·7	93·2
Output of milk fat on experimental days (as a % of output on control days)	100·0	100·0	114·2	81·7

Note: One star in the "Experimental days" column indicates that the best milking procedure was used, two stars that the teat was squeezed with the fingers 60 times per minute; each quarter of the udder was milked dry in turn. The numbering of the experimental days corresponds to that of the control days.

It was further necessary to verify the hypothesis that the efficiency of conditioned reflexes in milk ejection when consolidated by prolonged systematic reinforcements is dependent on the strength of the latter, i.e. on the quality of milking. We therefore conducted special experiments with three cows tended by P., who worked on the same farm as R. and had also tended these cows for three or more years before the experiment. In this respect the cows tended by R. and P. were quite alike. P. was a considerably "worse" milker than R.: she only squeezed the teat 80 times a minute, with the fingers not the palm, and milked the rear quarters first and the forequarters 1–2 min. later, i.e. she milked the quarters of the udder out of sequence. In this experiment we were therefore able to study the effect of a further "worsening" and of an "improvement" in the unconditioned stimuli of milk ejection in relation to P.'s normal milking technique. The results of the experiments are shown in Table 9.

Unexpected introduction of optimum milking was very effective in P.'s cows and increased the output of milk fat by 14·2%. Deterioration in milking technique had a marked effect on the fat output, which declined by 18·3%. As noted, the differences between P.'s normal technique and the pessimum combination used in the experiment were not so great as in the case of R. One can therefore probably explain the result obtained in P.'s group by the fact that the conditioned reflex component of milk ejection had been less subject to reinforcement and was therefore less effective owing to the weakness of the constant unconditioned reflex influences.

In our experiments with the cows of R., T. and P. we varied the quality of milking (the strength of the unconditioned stimuli) unexpectedly and once only. We did not set ourselves the task of clarifying the effect of prolonged alteration in the quality of milking, since, as we were working under farming conditions, we could not carry on with an experiment which would certainly have led to a decline in the production indices. In any case, such an experiment was scarcely necessary since the significance of the quality of milking was already quite evident. There is nothing fundamentally new in our establishment in these experiments of the fact that strong stable conditioned reflexes are of greater significance in milk ejection than the unconditioned reflexes. Many similar facts have been established in relation to other unconditioned reflexes, especially the reflexes of the cardio-vascular system. We shall confine ourselves to two examples.

Delov and Petrova (1948), working with dogs in which a stable conditioned reflex had been produced to the injection of morphine, substituted nitroglycerine for the unconditioned stimulus (morphine) in one of the experiments. In this case the response reaction was typical of the former stimulus—morphine. The cross experiment gave similar results.

Pshonik (1952) observed a similar phenomenon in experiments with vascular conditioned reflexes in man. There was a vasoconstrictive reaction when the conditioned stimulus of a bell was systematically reinforced by the unconditioned stimulus of cold. The nature of this reaction did not change when heat, which typically gives a vasodilatory reaction, was substituted for cold.

Thus the possibility that conditioned stimuli may outweigh unconditioned stimuli when the latter are suddenly varied is not a property that is exclusive to the reflexes of the mammary gland.

Up till now we have been considering conditioned reflex influences on the act of milk ejection in relation to the whole complex of stimuli that may acquire the significance of a signal, i.e. the whole conditions of milking. It is, however, important to establish which elements in this complex are of particular significance. Furthermore, when dealing with the influence of conditioned stimuli on the efficiency of milk ejection, we did not establish which aspect of this complex act is mainly effected by the conditioned stimuli. It is clear that this is also a question of fundamental theoretical and practical importance. Unfortunately neither question has as yet been studied sufficiently systematically, especially on the most important subject—the cow. The effect of the cortical factors on milk ejection in goats has been studied by Grachev (1951b). In 1951 he published the results of his studies on the production of conditioned reflexes to posterior-pituitary extract in goats. A subcutaneous injection of 0·03–0·06 ml of posterior-pituitary extract per kg of body weight was given every other day. A catheter was first inserted in one of the teats and connected to a Hanicke counter. This made it possible to obtain a record of the amount of milk discharged over a period of time.

In the control experiments without posterior-pituitary extract 60·5 ml of milk were discharged in 40 min. Within 5–8 min of the injection of posterior-pituitary extract there was a marked increase in the milk discharged to as much as 300 ml in the same period of time.

If the injection was accompanied by a bell (to which the animal had previously been indifferent), 11–13 juxtapositions of the injection and the bell were sufficient to cause increased milk removal averaging 155 ml in 40 min when only the bell was sounded. The animal responded to the bell somewhat more rapidly than to posterior-pituitary extract, within 1·5–2 min at the most. The injection of physiological saline produced a similar effect.

There are serious difficulties in the way of an explanation of the facts given by Grachev. Firstly, the nature of the unconditioned reflex on the basis of which a conditioned reflex is being developed in this experiment is unclear. All that we yet know concerning the way in which posterior-pituitary extract (more accurately oxytocin) affects the motor apparatus of the udder suggests that it operates directly on the myoepithelium and that the nervous system need not be involved in the realisation of this effect. This is shown by the fact that posterior-pituitary extract can be fully effective in a totally denervated lobe of the udder (Tsakhaev, 1953) and even in an isolated perfused udder (Ely and Petersen, 1941). Even Grachev apparently shares this view, since in a later paper (1952b) he quite correctly refers to posterior-pituitary extract as "the physiological stimulus of the apparatus of milk removal that *operates through the blood*" (my emphasis—M.Z.).

How then can we view the production of a temporary connexion to posterior-pituitary extract?

In the final analysis the production of any conditioned reflex is simply a matter that the impulses which arise as a result of the conditioned stimulus become capable of reaching the effector organ by the same efferent pathway by which the effect of the unconditioned stimulus is also realised. The way in which a conditioned reflex to posterior-pituitary extract is developed would be quite explicable if the injected posterior-pituitary extract (oxytocin) operated via receptors or directly on the centres to produce an unconditioned reflex to the pituitary which stimulated the secretion of oxytocin and milk ejection. This would also explain the way in which the conditioned reflex arose. This hypothesis is, however, completely without proof.

In any case, the facts do not support the idea that posterior-pituitary extract has a stimulating neurotropic effect. Thus, Knodt and Petersen (1944) found that the repeated injection of posterior-pituitary extract failed to stimulate the oxytocic activity of the hypophysis in cows and even inhibited it and reduced the efficiency of "physiological" milk ejection.

There are certain facts which indicate that conditioned reflexes cannot be formed to the injection of posterior-pituitary extract. Thus Natochin (1955) was unable to produce a conditioned reflex to the antidiuretic effect of posterior-pituitary extract in experiments on dogs, although a conditioned reflex to water loading was easily created in the same animals, i.e. a conditioned reflex to an unconditioned stimulus that reflexly inhibits the antidiuretic activity of the hypophysis. This case is especially interesting since the antidiuretic effect of posterior-pituitary extract, like the oxytocic effect, is not neurotropic but is brought about by direct influence on the effector. Whittlestone (1953a) notes particularly from repeated tests of standard doses of oxytocin in sows that in repeated injection of sows with oxytocin in doses sufficient to cause milk ejection he never once observed "spontaneous" milk ejection either when the animal was brought to the stall where the tests were normally carried out or when physiological saline was injected in place of oxytocin, although, as he observes, these experiments provided every basis for the formation of a conditioned reflex to milk ejection. Further examples could be cited if it was necessary to our purpose.

The matter is even more complicated since posterior-pituitary extract generally possesses the property of inhibiting the switching activity of the cerebral cortex.

Asratyan (1935) has shown that firmly established salivary reflexes in dogs are greatly weakened or completely lost on the injection of posterior-pituitary extract. Danilov (1940) found very much the same in dogs with electrocutaneous defence conditioned reflexes, as also did Gorodetskaya (1953) in doves with established defence conditioned reflexes.

Posterior-pituitary extract does not only affect conditioned reflexes that are already developed. Natochin (1955), for example, found that simultaneous injection of posterior-pituitary extract prevents the development of a conditioned reflex to diuresis (water loading). It is difficult to explain why this inhibitory effect of posterior-pituitary extract is not manifested when one attempts to produce a conditioned reflex to its own action, as in Grachev's experiments.

All that has just been said leads one to assume that the enhanced discharge of milk in these experiments was not associated with a conditioned reflex to posterior-pituitary extract, but was due to other causes. It may, for example, be assumed that the subcutaneous injection of posterior-pituitary extract caused a pain reaction and movement of the animal that led to increased milk discharge. Grachev himself correctly emphasises this significance in the movements of a goat in other papers.

In other experiments by Grachev (1952b) a conditioned milk discharge reflex was also produced to a bell, when combined with an unconditioned stimulus—mechanical stimuli of the teat in sham milking. In this same series of experiments it was found that the conditions under which the experiments are carried out acquire the importance of a signal. One proof of this is that when the goat was brought to the room where the experimental milking was carried out there was an increase in the cisternal portion of the milk and a corresponding decline in the alveolar portion. Grachev treats this as the reflexly conditioned movement of milk into the cistern before milking commences. When the goat was taken to another "indifferent" room this did not occur.

In these experiments the author succeeded in showing the importance of negative differentiating stimuli and also the importance of stimuli new to the animal that when first employed inhibited both the conditioned reflexes that had been produced and the unconditioned reflexes. In this respect he fully confirmed the findings of Voskresenskii (1916, 1917) on cows. Voskresenskii was the first to establish the role of the cerebral cortex in the act of milk removal.

Grachev's experiments, which were conducted by all the rules of the classic Pavlovian method, unquestionably established that the cerebral cortex affects milk removal. But when one analyses his results one cannot always establish sufficiently clearly which aspect of the complex act of milk ejection he is speaking of in the given case; it is not always clear whether we are concerned with the entry of milk into the cistern from the ducts or with a movement due to the contraction of the alveoli. Grachev himself does not consider these two mechanisms separately.

This latter question has been somewhat clarified by Borsuk (1955b) in experiments on cows and by Gofman (1955) in experiments on goats. They have both established that conditioned reflexes for milk ejection mainly evoke not contraction of the alveoli but the reaction of the musculature of the ducts which facilitates the entry of milk into the cisterns. Conditioned reflex contraction of the alveoli is very difficult to produce and is unstable and easily inhibited, especially when using the artificial stimuli (bells, buzzers, etc.) normally used in such experiments. It is true that Grachev was more concerned with the development of a conditioned reflex to the alveoli, but it is possible that goats may differ from cows in this respect. In any case, Borsuk has quite clearly distinguished between these two phenomena—reaction of the ducts and contraction of the alveoli—each of which gives rise to an effect that would appear to be similar, namely the entry of milk into the cistern. These two conditioned reflexes are even more clearly distinguished in later papers by Borsuk (1957). The distinguishing features of the first reflex to the ducts are the rapidity with which it can be produced (after 4–5 juxtapositions), its stability and the fact that it can be externally inhibited with ease. The second reflex to the alveoli, which can only be produced with difficulty by many juxtapositions, is moreover unstable.

It is clear that feeding is of particular significance as a conditioned stimulus of milk ejection. Espe (1946) refers to a cow which was always given its concentrates immediately before milking. When the animal happened to injure the sphincter of one of the teats milk entering the cistern flowed out freely. The cow therefore had to be milked at the same time as it was fed to avoid great losses of milk from the quarter with the damaged sphincter. Since these losses occurred during feeding it is clear that we are concerned with alveolar milk or with the forced discharge of milk from the ducts into the cistern.

Syusyukin (1955), who used feeding as a conditioned stimulus, established that after the formation of a stable reflex almost all the alveolar milk was to be found in the cisterns even before milking commenced after the conditioned stimulus had been applied. It is clear that Syusyukin's attempt to develop a conditioned reflex contraction of the alveoli was successful in these experiments precisely because the conditioned stimulus—feeding—which he selected was sufficiently adequate. Syusyukin's findings will undoubtedly be of importance in solving the whole problem of the extent to which feeding and milking can be combined. Many animal husbandry experts oppose this combination on the grounds that feeding "distracts" the cow from milking; i.e., physiologically speaking, the existence of excitation in the food centre lowers the efficiency of specific stimuli of the mammary gland. We now have reason to believe that this fear is without foundation. On the contrary, the detailed studies of Grachev (1952a) and work in Azimov's laboratory (Orlov, 1955) show that there are special nervous connexions between digestion and lactation which are in no way antagonistic. There can scarcely therefore be any physiological contraindications to the combination of feeding and milking. Such obstacles as may exist are concerned with hygiene rather than with physiology: there is, for example, a danger that the milk may be contaminated.

Further studies should show whether feeding is the only conditioned stimulus with which a conditioned reflex contraction of the alveoli can be fairly easily produced or whether other stimuli also have this property. In the meantime we continue to assume that it is fairly difficult to develop a conditioned reflex contraction of the alveoli. It may be thought that the difficulties associated with the development of such a reflex are not accidental and that they have a definite biological basis. In the overwhelming majority of mammals, suckling by the young is associated with considerable exertion; the young animal takes quite a time to obtain the milk that it needs. Experts in the rearing of calves know from experience that the best results are obtained when the milk is taken slowly through the teat or from a special feeder: this enhances the secretion of gastric juices and the milk is digested faster and more completely.

According to Popov (Azimov, Krinitsin and Popov, 1954) saliva is much more plentifully secreted when the calf takes the milk slowly. The milk is well mixed with the saliva and this helps the formation of small granulated clots of casein in the stomach, whereas compact clots are formed when the milk is taken rapidly. Slow drinking is equally favourable to gastric digestion; in these conditions the lips of the oesophageal groove are most tightly closed. It should be remembered that slight interruptions in the evacuation of the udder lead to the milk with the lowest fat content, which will have the least effect in reducing the secretion of gastric juice, being suckled first.

If a conditioned reflex contraction of the alveoli could be produced easily, such factors as the smell, appearance, sound and approach of the young would undoubtedly come to be a signal for every animal and milk ejection would be fully developed before feeding commenced. This would remove a natural obstacle to the suckling of milk which is of definite physiological importance to the young. This, in my opinion, is why the function of contraction of the alveoli has been so developed in the course of mammalian evolution that it is mainly produced by unconditioned rather than conditioned stimuli directly associated with the act of suckling. Even in the case of the unconditioned reflex there often seems to be some obstacle to its development.

The significance of this specific inertia of the unconditioned reflex contraction of the alveoli can be seen most clearly in pigs. Kvasnitskii and Konyukhova (1954) write that it takes not less than 7–10 min of hard work by the piglets in suckling empty teats and massaging the sow's udder before the milk ejection reflex develops. Milk ejection itself only lasts for 30–40 sec and the same amount of time is taken in suckling the milk. It is clear that the rapidity of suckling in this case does not have a negative effect on the piglet since the amount of milk in one feeding is very small—each piglet only receives 20–30 g. In addition, one can easily imagine that the preliminary manipulations of the udder by the piglet in search of food will have caused energetic secretion of gastric juice. We should add that there is another distinctive feature to milk ejection in the sow. Milk ejection does not develop throughout the udder simultaneously but spreads from the front to the rear teats. This process normally takes 5–6 sec, but may last as much as 20 sec in some sows. A few piglets are able to drain their teat and rush to one of the rear teats before milk ejection ceases. It is possible that the relationship between the nervous and hormonal factors in milk ejection is not the same in sows as in ruminants, but this question needs further study.

In addition to the scientific data cited there is a great deal of purely empirical material to show that cortical reactions are undoubtedly involved in milk ejection. None of this information however explains which peripheral mechanism is responsible for these reactions. I have in mind such well known and well attested facts as the free flow of milk from cows that are easy to milk when milking time is near or when the milkmaid approaches. It is likely that these are not cases of complete milk ejection but of a conditioned reflex relaxation in the teat sphincters or supplementary entry of milk into the cisterns from the ducts.

I have often had to study the cisternal and alveolar portions separately in cows when the experiment was preceded by normal farming preparation for the next milking, i.e. when a conditioned reflex to milking conditions which would give rise to contraction of the alveoli could appear if it had been developed in these animals. In no single case from the thousands of observations now made can it be said with absolute certainty that there was a conditioned reflex contraction of the alveoli. Nevertheless the conditioned reflex movement of milk into the cistern from the ducts is observed so frequently that special measures have to be taken to avert it in some experiments. It is true that all our observations were made on cows milked three or four times a day, and that the udder was not therefore greatly overfilled.

This does not mean, of course, that it is generally impossible to produce a conditioned reflex contraction of the alveoli. There is no reason to think that the unconditioned reflex of milk ejection is a completely inexplicable exception to the general Pavlovian rule that a conditioned reflex can be produced to any function of the organism. The point is that this conditioned reflex is either difficult to produce or, possibly, is easily inhibited. It is also possible that in all the experiments and observations mentioned above in which this difficulty was encountered, it was simply a question that the conditions most favourable to the production and manifestation of a conditioned reflex of this type had not been found. From this point of view new data by Kokorina (1956a, b) are of great interest. She has undoubtedly succeeded in producing a conditioned reflex that brings about total evacuation of the storage system of the udder in some cows. In her experiments normal milking was the unconditioned stimulus and the conditions of milking provided the conditioned stimulus. According to Kokorina the nature of the conditioned reflex (speed with which it can be produced, liability to inhibition, etc.) in individual cows bears a definite relationship to the previously established type features of the animals selected for the experiments.

Kokorina's experiments differ fundamentally from those of her predecessors in that her experiments were conducted a considerable time (up to 12 hr) after the previous milking, i.e. when the lactational centre was in a high state of excitation. It may be thought by analogy with conditioned food reflexes that this circumstance is of great importance and facilitates the development of the conditioned reflex. This hypothesis is supported by Grachev's findings (already cited) that prolongation of the interval between milkings is of undoubted significance for the efficiency of milk injection in goats.

Shvabe (1956) arrives at an absolutely similar conclusion. He established that the completeness of milk ejection in cows is increased when the interval between milkings is extended, whilst the rate of synthesis of milk and of milk fat in particular is lowered.

In addition to its positive influences which stimulate milk ejection and enhance the efficiency of its unconditioned stimuli, the cerebral cortex can also exert retarding and inhibitory influences on milk ejection. We have already given some examples of a similar type when dealing with the positive cortical influences.

Duplications of this type cannot be avoided, since in experiments, as in life, excitation and inhibition and the positive and negative influences of the cerebral cortex are intimately connected. Unfortunately it is often the inhibitory influences of the cerebral cortex on milk ejection that are encountered in the dairy farm. An attentive observer will see all types of examples of these inhibitory effects that often seriously interfere with both hand and machine milking in a cattle yard at milking time. Voskresenskii was the first person to evaluate the significance of these facts correctly and to treat them in a truly Pavlovian manner.

The most diverse agents can inhibit milk ejection. It is common knowledge that any unusual event in the cattle yard at milking time, which disturbs the accustomed routine of the animals, will invariably be reflected in a decline in the overall figures for cream and in the total yield. Any stimulus that causes a sufficiently strong orientating reaction in the cow may lead to the inhibition of milk ejection. After it has been repeated a number of times a stimulus of this type loses its inhibitory effect (Voskresenskii). It is true that the reactivity of cows to these inhibitory stimuli varies. There are animals in which even the most insignificant deviation from the normal milking pattern will inhibit milk ejection. On one Karelian state farm that I have seen, approximately 10% of the cows will only give milk at milking time if they are given a heaped handful of salted flour or bran before milking begins. This feeding has become such a firmly established part of the milking pattern for these animals that milk ejection is inhibited without fail if it is withdrawn. Change of milkmaid, the wrong time and sequence of milking, a change in the milkmaid's usual position when milking and similar factors have a similar effect on some cows.

Nevertheless there are cows in which neither conditioned agents nor even such unconditioned agents as a sharp pain stimulus when an injured teat is milked have much of a retarding effect on milk ejection, even although the pain stimulus evokes a general defence reaction in the animal. A detailed study of the cortical mechanisms by which milk ejection is inhibited is of considerable practical significance.

It is certain that cases of the cortical inhibition of milk ejection are encountered more frequently than conditioned reflex milk ejection. Apparently a far wider range of stimuli can become signals for inhibition, whereas positive conditioned reflexes for milk ejection, unlike those for the salivary gland, are formed in response to a more restricted range of stimuli. It is also possible that the comparative ease with which an orientating and conditioned inhibition of milk ejection can occur has phylogenetic roots. The wild ancestors of the cow and, in all probability, a number of other mammals would have derived a clear biological advantage from this ease in the inhibition of milk ejection, since on the approach of danger the female would be able to "curtail" feeding rapidly and switch to defence reactions. The inhibition of milk ejection may take the most varied forms. It is most frequently expressed in a considerable extension of the latent period of the reflex, which may be prolonged by four or five times or even more by an inhibitory agent. It should be remembered that some cows already have a relatively prolonged latent period.

The latent period is sometimes so extended that the cow cannot be milked at all at milking time. Moreover, milk ejection which has already commenced may be temporarily or entirely halted, although this is a less frequent occurrence. Finally another distinctive form of the inhibition of milk ejection in which the rate of the reaction is considerably slowed down and there is a sharp fall in the rate at which the cow gives its milk, may sometimes be noted after the reaction has commenced. In this connexion it should be borne in mind that according to Savel'ev (1947, 1949), there can be great variations in different animals in the rate at which an active reaction to milking develops. Savel'ev classifies cows on this basis into slow, normal and brisk "types". In Savel'ev's view the following are the main distinctions between cows with slow and brisk milk ejection. With identical udder capacity determined by Azimov's method (approximately 11 l) and almost the same yield from a single milking (7·77 and 7·71 l) machine milking lasted 10·26 min in the former and 6·77 min in the latter. The average yield per minute was 0·757 and 1·138 l respectively. Hand stripping was approximately the same in both. Cows of the brisk type have a markedly glandular type of udder.

Savel'ev assumes that these features are associated with the typological differences of the cows and draws a number of practical conclusions: that cows with brisk milk ejection should be milked first, that there should be individual rather than standard methods of preparing for milking with cows of the different types, etc. Time will show to what extent these differences are associated with the type of higher nervous activity of the animals, but some of the author's practical suggestions cannot be disputed.

Kokorina has studied the effect of the type of higher nervous activity (HNA) on the motor function of the mammary gland (1956a, b, 1958, 1959a, 1959b, 1959c).

The type of HNA was established by the motor-food method in a simple Pavlov chamber, the internal layout of which was similar to that of the cow's normal stall. The animal obtained food from a feeder which gave a supply when the animal pressed a disc, i.e. in response to a movement similar to the "obtaining" of water from an automatic waterbowl. The food was given after the operation of a conditioned stimulus, which was either auditory or visual. This method enabled Kokorina to describe the dynamics of the two main cortical processes—excitation and inhibition—in relation to their strength, versatility and balance. On the basis of these indices she divides the cows into groups in accordance with the Pavlovian classification of types of HNA; (1) weak, (2) strong, balanced and versatile, (3) strong, balanced and inert, (4) strong and unbalanced. There are, of course, various intermediate forms associated with these basic types. Kokorina established a correlation between the type of HNA and the nature of the udder's capacity function (i.e. the processes that regulate the movement of milk in the storage system in the interval between milkings). She also traces a similar correlation with the milk-ejection reflex. The milk-ejection reflex is more stable and diurnal fluctuations in the yield and percentage of milk fat are less marked in cows of the strong, balanced and versatile type than in those of the balanced, inert and unbalanced types. Inhibition of milk removal and of the conditioned reflexes associated with milk ejection as a result of various influences that disturb normal conditions are also less marked than in the other types. In animals of the weak type such influences as sudden sharp sounds or light stimuli or the insertion of a milk catheter etc. may inhibit both the motor reactions of the mammary gland and its secretory activity.

Similar studies have been carried out by Aizenbudas (1957a, 1957b, 1957c, 1958). The type of HNA was determined when the animal was free to move about (free motor method) by the Gurevich and Kolesnikov tests (1955) in a large pen 30 × 15 m. Before the animals were put into the pen portions of food were placed in one or two feeders installed on the ground by the rear wall of the pen. The quantitative index of the conditioned reflex was the speed with which the animal made its way from the entrance to the pen to the food point. A time record was made of the animal's motor activity with a special automatic recorder fastened to its back. It was possible to create different conditions for studying differentiation of stimuli and alteration in their significance by changing the position of a charged or empty feeder. In these conditions the motor-food conditioned reflexes were subordinated to the laws established for salivary conditioned reflexes.

Like Kokorina, Aizenbudas establishes a positive correlation between the typological feature of the HNA and the physiological characteristics of the motor function of the mammary gland. Animals with highly stable and versatile cortical processes normally show the least diurnal fluctuations in milk yield and fat content. The processes of milk removal are less subject in them to inhibition due to the disturbance of normal conditions such as milking technique. The dynamics of the rise in fat percentage in successive portions of a single milking in cows of the strong, stable, versatile type are extremely constant and do not vary greatly when the pattern of milking conditions is disturbed. In weak, inert, unstable cows, on the other hand, there can easily be variation in the fat percentage in the successive portions of a milking. It has also been discovered that there are considerable variations in the level of blood lipids in animals with high diurnal fluctuations in fat percentage in the milk. The main conclusions to be drawn from the findings of Aizenbudas and Kokorina are the same although the procedures and the animals were different.

The theory of milk ejection. In the light of the facts set out above I must briefly review earlier and existing theories of milk ejection before ending this section. The first theory of milk ejection, in point of time, was the "secretory" theory, according to which the removal of milk is largely an expression of its enhanced secretion at the moment of milking. At all events Duerst (1931), who has given the most explicit formulation of this theory, assumed that as much as three-quarters of a single milking can be made up in this manner in some cows.

There is no need to recount all the arguments which have been advanced from time to time in support of the secretory theory; most of them are now of purely historical interest. The majority of authors now consider that there is no fundamental increase in the secretion of milk at the moment of milk ejection.

Nevertheless one can still not decisively reject all the elements in the secretory theory or assert that the secretory component plays no role in milk ejection and, in particular, that no secretion of milk occurs at this time. The concept of the "time of milk formation" is still open to discussion and some authors still hold the view that some part of the milk is formed during milking. Thus, Ogorodnii (1953) assumes that up to 30% of the yield can be obtained in this manner in certain cases. Sineshchekov (1956b) holds the same view.

It is certain that the categorical denial by some authors including myself (Zaks, 1950) that this factor has any significance is now in need of certain qualification. In the first place the very concept of "milk secretion" needs to be made somewhat more precise.[1] "Milk secretion" is normally taken to be the process by which synthesized milk is removed from the secretory cells into the cavities of the storage system, but this is only the end result of a series of complex processes which precede it, and it will therefore be more correct to extend the concept of "milk secretion" to the following main processes:

(1) uptake of the specific precursors of milk from the blood by the secretory cells of the mammary gland;

(2) their synthetic conversion into the end products: casein, milk fat, lactose, etc.;

(3) the concentrating work of the mammary gland, which leads to the content of some ions (Ca, P, K, Mg) being considerably higher

---

[1] Espe (1946) distinguishes between the secretory and excretory activity of the mammary gland, but this is not entirely accurate terminologically, since excretion is normally understood as the removal of the end products of metabolism from the organism. It is probable that this confusion in concepts explains why the mammary gland is considered in the same section as the skin in relation to the excretory function as a whole in certain textbooks of physiology.

and of others (Cl, Na) being lower in the milk than in the blood plasma;

(4) joint removal of the water-soluble and water-insoluble components of the milk with water into the storage system.

The substances that move into the lumen of the alveoli may have been synthesized immediately before discharge or may have been stored and accumulated after synthesis in the cytoplasm of the secretory cells for varying periods. It is clear that the possibility of storage is far from being the same for the different components of the milk.

To decide whether or not it is possible for any considerable quantities of milk to move from the cells into the alveoli in the 10-15 min taken in the preparation for milking and milking of the highest-yielding cows (the duration of active milk ejection being even shorter), one does not need to consider milk secretion as a whole, but the significance of all the processes which are comprised by the secretory activity of the mammary gland.

In the first place one must distinguish between the synthesis of milk substances from their precursors and the discharge into the storage system in the form of the prepared secretion—milk—of substances synthesized earlier and deposited in the cells. All the latest data obtained by the use of labelled atoms lead us to assume that it is not very likely that there can be any considerable intensification in the volume of synthesis from precursors at the moment of milking. Thus, Kleiber (1954) found that when various milk precursors labelled with ^{14}C (glucose, various fatty acids, acetates, carbonates, etc.) were intravenously injected into lactating cows, the intensive appearance in the milk of synthesized products labelled with radioactive carbon only commenced in the third hour for casein and even later by about the seventh hour for fat. Azimov (1955) found from experiments involving the injection of phosphate labelled with ^{32}P that it was at least an hour before specific activity was detected in casein and three hours for the phospholipids associated with milk fat. Allowing for all possible errors in these calculations due to the presence of residual milk,[1] the processes of milk synthesis from precursors can nevertheless be said to be fairly slow and to require considerable time and there is no real basis for expecting serious quantitative shifts within 5 min.

[1] This was allowed for in Azimov's experiments.

The removal of products already synthesized and deposited in the cells can be quite a different matter. Here the possible efficiency of the secretory process will be mainly determined by the size of the mobile reserve of the substances. The size of this reserve can be most accurately assessed for fat, but since it is a question of basic significance we shall deal with it in a separate chapter.

Azimov (1955) considers that sufficient casein is deposited in the cytoplasm of the alveolar cells to ensure that the gland can function for 2 hr without additional synthesis.

Gaines and Saanmann (1927) found that the total lactose content of the udder was 20% greater than the amount in a single milking; this difference can hardly be entirely covered by the residual milk. Although Gowen and Tobey (1928) did not discover lactose in the udder of a nonlactating cow, this does not prove that it cannot be deposited in a functioning gland. Thus, one can assume that the principal organic components of milk can be stored in the gland in sufficient quantities for there to be some possible increase in secretion at the moment of milk ejection. The inorganic components can also scarcely limit this process by themselves, since they are in the main already combined with proteins and fat from the moment that the latter are synthesized and deposited.

One must dwell specially on the water in milk, which is its main mass by volume. It would appear that water is the main factor which limits the formation of considerable quantities of milk in a short time, since there is only a limited possibility for its deposition in the secretory cells and its main source can only be the plasma of the incoming blood. Simple filtration, as a result of hydrostatic pressure differences between the circulatory capillaries and the cavities of the alveoli cannot be of fundamental significance, mainly because of the marked disequilibrium in the concentration of the various ions in the blood plasma and the milk. Simple physical filtration would, moreover, be complicated by the purely morphological properties of the alveolar epithelium. In this respect the alveoli cannot be compared either with tissue capillaries or with renal glomeruli, where both the morphological properties of the separating membranes and the total ionic balance of the blood plasma and the filtrate (tissue fluid or provisional urine) make physical filtration quite possible, since it is only necessary to overcome the oncotic pressure of the blood plasma proteins.

Thus the movement of water from the blood into the milk can only be due in the main to the secretory activity of the epithelium of the mammary gland. Physical processes can here play only a subsidiary rather than a basic role. We shall see later that this circumstance is of great importance.

It is useful to remember that one of the main objections advanced against the secretion of milk during milking is that the vascular network of the udder cannot pass the amount of blood essential for the formation of the required amounts of milk in such a short time. For example, Espe (1946) writes quite categorically concerning the possibility of a considerable intensification in secretion at the time of milking: "No physiological process could be conceived which would synthesize milk this fast. In fact, the mere removal of the required amount of water from the blood for such a rapid synthesis would cause the blood to congeal unless the pulse rate increased." These objections are mainly based on data concerning the arteriovenous difference in the main milk precursors and on the assumption that the udder is inadequately supplied with blood; they hold in relation to the rate at which the organic substances of milk are synthesized.

An estimate of the possibility of the secretion of water is a quite different matter. A simple calculation shows that this process can scarcely be limited by inadequacy of the blood supply. In fact, calculations of the arteriovenous difference show that approximately 10,000 kg of blood pass through the udder of a high-yielding cow in 24 hr. This is approximately 7 kg a minute. Approximately 50%, or 3500 g, is plasma and it can be assumed that if the mammary gland extracted approximately 350–400 ml of water a minute from the blood plasma this would not greatly increase the viscosity of the blood and would not have a significant effect on its further movement through the vessels. This output of water more than covers the requirements even of a quite intense secretory process.

The question may arise as to whether the mammary gland is capable of using this amount of water for secretion.

Here we must have recourse to analogy with other glands that secrete solutions that are not isotonic with the blood, even analogy with the salivary glands. It is well known that the salivary glands of a cow, for example, secrete approximately 50 ml of saliva a minute, and that the total weight of the gland is very much less than that of the udder. Azimov (1955) has calculated that the working surface of the alveoli of the udder is approximately 1 m². He thinks that this area is quite sufficient to ensure the transition of considerable amounts of water into the milk even by simple filtration. But the capacity of this working surface will be even greater if the movement of water is due to the specific secretory activity of the cells of the alveolar epithelium.

The final conclusion to be drawn is that there are a number of possibilities in the mammary gland for certain quantities of milk to move from the cytoplasm of the cells into the cavities of the alveoli in a short space of time at the expense of deposited reserves of its main components. Nor can it be doubted that under certain conditions this "secretory" factor may play some role in the process of milk ejection. All the objections and arguments that have been put forward are, of course, conditional. I have only cited them to show that there is no reason to consider that the possibility of an intensification in the secretion of milk at the moment of milking has been finally and unequivocally refuted. The purpose of these objections is to show that further painstaking research will help to solve the problem. This research must be undertaken since the possible effect of milking on the secretion of the mammary gland is of fundamental practical interest in addition to being of theoretical significance.

According to Hammond (1936) most of the energy that expels milk from the alveoli arises from the inflow of blood into the gland. From this point of view milk ejection is treated as a distinctive haemodynamic reflex, in the course of which there is simultaneous dilatation of the arteries and contraction of the veins in response to stimuli of the udder receptors. In Hammond's opinion this leads to a rise in blood pressure in the capillaries around the alveoli sufficient to "expel" milk out of the alveoli into the ducts. The vascular network of the udder is in fact extremely extensive. It is also known that there is a considerable increase in the flow of blood to the udder during milking (Vladimirova, 1955). Nevertheless, a factual examination of the haemodynamic conditions that develop around each separate alveolus leads me to conclude that the mechanism suggested by Hammond can scarcely be of fundamental significance. In actual fact the diameter of each completely full alveolus is approximately 300μ; the capillary network around the alveolus is dense but "monolayered", and the capillaries of which it is composed are not markedly different in thickness from ordinary tissue capillaries, i.e. their diameters are measured in microns. Even when expanded to the maximum, and allowing for the opening of additional closed capillaries, they could not squeeze much milk out of the alveoli and could hardly compress the diameter of the alveoli by more than 20 or at most 30%. No structures similar, for example, to the spaces in spongy tissue, which would make possible fairly considerable compression of the alveoli and expulsion of their contents, have been identified in the surrounding area. It follows that no increase in blood pressure in the capillaries could play as important a role as that ascribed to it by Hammond's theory.

Nevertheless, one cannot entirely deny that increased filling of the udder with blood and an increase in turgescence in the vicinity of the alveoli may create conditions favourable to the development of the basic processes associated with the liberation of milk from the alveoli. The significance of the haemodynamic factor in milk ejection is further complicated by the findings of Pickles (1953, 1954), who has established that in the woman there is a decline and not an increase in the flow of blood into the mammary gland at the moment of milk ejection. These facts tend to contradict the findings of Vladimirova, who was, however, working on a different subject under different experimental conditions.

The neurohumoral theory of Ely and Petersen, which has been outlined above, correctly emphasises the importance of the reflex mechanism of milk ejection and the significance of conditioned reflexes. As already noted, the theory does not allow correctly for the role of the humoral link in the reaction (the posterior pituitary hormone) and also assumes incorrectly that milk ejection is independent of efferent nervous influences. The new facts now established enable us to supplement the theory of Ely and Petersen. I feel that the merit of my outline is that while retaining the rational kernel in the theory of my predecessors it allows more fully for the nervous regulation of milk ejection and takes into consideration all the links in nervous regulations, including the higher cortical link. Its main distinguishing features are the new conception of milk ejection as a two stage act, which is formulated on p. 65 and of the role of direct efferent innervation of the motor apparatus of the udder and direct mechanical stimulation of its contractile elements.

CHAPTER THREE

FEATURES OF THE PRODUCTION OF MILK FAT AND OTHER MILK CONSTITUENTS

Variations in fat content in the milk of a single milking. In our examination of the process by which the storage system of the udder is filled and of the act of milk ejection we have, as yet, scarcely touched on differences in the composition of milk in the separate parts of the gland's storage system or on the composition of the successive portions of a single milking. It stands to reason that any gland possesses the property of being able to vary the chemical composition of its secretion in relation to the stimuli that cause secretion and to a number of other conditions. Nevertheless, the mammary gland of many mammals differs fundamentally from other glands of external secretion in that the composition of successive portions of its secretion—the milk removed in a single act of milk ejection—is always different. This feature of the mammary gland is of great significance, since a detailed study of its causes will enable us to understand a number of processes concerned with milk synthesis and will make it possible to rationalize milking methods and increase the efficiency of milking.

It is well known that the fat content of separate portions of milk from a single milking is subject to marked variations. It is also common knowledge that there are far greater variations in the percentage of fat, in milkings at the same time of day on different days, than in the "liquid" part of the milk and its water-soluble components. This is clearly due in large measure to fluctuations in the processes of fat synthesis in the mammary gland, but it is just as connected with the removal of already-synthesized fat. Azimov (1955) was certainly quite correct to state that "milk is secreted entire and not as separate components". One may, however, consider that there may be somewhat different degrees of interdependence between the separate components. From the moment of its synthesis in the cytoplasm of the alveolar cells, milk fat, in Azimov's words, "has its own particular subsequent path". Since it is not soluble in milk plasma and is osmotically inactive, milk fat is the most "independent" component of milk, by comparison with any other osmotically active component: the ions, lactose and, lastly, proteins that determine the colloidal and osmotic nature of the milk. Changes in the synthesis of any of these latter components and in their transfer from the cells must inescapably affect the ratio of the other osmotically active components. This is essential if the milk and the blood are to remain iso-osmotic, which is clearly an important physiological condition for milk synthesis. We shall first consider the fluctuations in fat content throughout a single milking.

As already stated, changes in the intensity of synthesis alone can scarcely account for fluctuations in the fat content of a milking: these fluctuations are clearly considerably affected by removal from the gland of already-synthesized fat. This is particularly applicable to fluctuations that arise as a result of definite stimuli on the animal immediately before milking. Anyone concerned with the practical management of dairy cows will have observed similar fluctuations. The percentage of fat in the milk may be considerably decreased (more often) or considerably increased (less frequently) on a dairy farm when some attendant factor disturbs the milking pattern to which the animal is accustomed. Thus, Olenov found in our laboratory that when a cow with its first calf was milked by a substitute milker who seriously infringed the rules of milking by greatly altering the rate of milking to which the animal was accustomed and changing the sequence in which the quarters were milked, the fat content was sharply reduced from 3·2% on average for the midday milking to 1%. The decline in the total volume of the milk yield was insignificant and could in no way be compared with the decrease in the percentage of fat. In Azimov's laboratory (1955) a decline in the percentage of fat was observed when the strong and unusual stimulus of a bell ringing combined with the flashing of an electric torch was applied immediately before milking.

In the course of exact experiments in which conditioned reflexes were produced for the discharge of milk in response to massage and washing the udder, Borsuk (1955a) noticed that when the developed conditioned reflex was inhibited there was a marked change in the results of the next milking. The percentage of fat in the alveolar portion was sharply reduced, as was the total percentage of fat in the yield as a whole, although the volume of the yield was less significantly affected. In one such experiment, for example, the decline in the total amount of fat removed was 39·9%, whilst the yield only declined by 3·2%. The average volume of the yield and the overall output of fat in the same milking on previous days were taken as 100%.

Ogorodnii (1953) found that under the two-shift system of management the sharpest fluctuations in fat content on different days occurred after the short 3-hour intervals and that these fluctuations were considerably reduced when the same cows were milked at equal intervals. (Under the two-shift system the cows are milked four times a day, usually at 4 a.m., 7 a.m., 4 p.m. and 7 p.m., the farm staff being on duty from 4 a.m. to 8 a.m. and 4 p.m. to 8 p.m.—Editor).

Further examples could be given but I need only stress that lack of agreement between concurrent fluctuations in the size of the yield and the total output of milk fat is not uncommon.

Practical workers likewise know that similar fluctuations in fat content in separate milkings may little affect daily fat output as deficiencies are largely made good in subsequent milkings. Such fluctuations are thus associated rather with the removal of fat than with its synthesis.

We also know of examples of the reverse case, although these are certainly much less frequent, in which unusual stimuli affecting the animal between milkings or at milking time lead to a marked increase in the percentage of fat when the volume of the yield remains relatively stable. An example of this type is cited by Zaks and Borsuk (1955a), who found that fat content increased to more than 6%, as against the normal 3–3·2%, in one cow being used for experiments when the animal was subjected to a situation leading to the creation of neurosis*: on this day the normal experiment involving prolonged catheterization coincided with a slight injury to another teat while at pasture: although the injured teat was not

* We say that this situation created a neurosis since the after-effect was very marked. The cow, which had previously been absolutely docile, began to react most aggressively to any attempt to insert the catheter, and was for long unsuitable for experiments involving catheterization. It is typical that, from later study, Kokorina classified this animal as one with a weak type of higher nervous activity.

catheterized, the animal reacted to normal insertion of the catheter in the adjacent teat by marked and prolonged agitation.

Polivoda (1955) observed that when goats were called upon to "solve problems" that were too difficult for their higher nervous activity on days following experiments in a conditioned reflex chamber there was sometimes a distinct increase in the output of butter fat when the animal was milked several hours after the experiment. It is true that Polivoda's results are also connected to a considerable extent with changes in the processes of fat synthesis.

All these facts show that the removal of milk fat has some special features that distinguish it from removal of the liquid part of the milk and that are associated with certain special mechanisms. If these mechanisms can be discovered it will be of great practical importance, since the main task of correct milking is precisely to extract the maximum quantity of milk fat from the udder and thus stimulate its further synthesis.

The percentage of fat in the successive portions of a single milking. The reasons for differences in fat content in the successive portions of a single milking are of the greatest significance for an understanding of these mechanisms. The fact itself has long been known. As long ago as 1849 Reiset found from a study of the first and subsequent portions of the yield of two cows that there were considerable differences in the fat content. This was apparently the first time that this had been established. The differences ranged from 1–2% in the first portion up to 13% in the subsequent portion. Similar results were later obtained by Schmidt-Mülheim (1883), Rose and Winter (1934), Pritsker (1941), Inikhov (1951) and many other investigators. Till now, however, the mechanism of this phenomenon has not been explained and even its description is to some extent incomplete.

It is widely believed that the percentage of fat increases as successive portions of milk are obtained: the percentage of fat is lowest in the first streams of milk and highest in the last portions— the strippings obtained after final massage. According to this view, the percentage of fat will be even higher in the residual milk, which can only be removed after the injection of the requisite dose of posterior-pituitary extract. It is also considered that the variation in the percentage of fat in the successive portions follows an ascending curve (Rikhter, 1939; Espe, 1946; Solov'ev, 1952), but that fat is evenly distributed in the residual milk. I shall show subsequently that these widely-held views need to be basically re-examined in the light of new facts established by myself and other investigators; but we must first examine the principal theories that attempt to explain the reasons for this puzzling phenomenon.

The first to be put forward was the "creaming" theory, according to which the increase in the percentage of fat in successive portions of a single yield was to be explained simply by the settling of the fat in the storage system. This hypothesis has had a very distinctive history. It is difficult at this stage to say who was its originator, although it was repeatedly advanced from the second half of the nineteenth century onwards. It is, for example, mentioned, although certainly critically, by Heidenhain (1886, p. 525). Armsby (1917) returned to it thirty years later. Ragsdale, Brody and Turner (1921) tried to provide the hypothesis with an experimental foundation, but their experiment was conducted on a single cow and the successive portions of the yield were taken after two hours quiet standing in the cattle yard, immediately after return from pasture, after massage and under other conditions. They made a parallel study of the way in which the fat in the milk of the same cow separated out when it was allowed to stand in a cylinder. They concluded that movement and massage lead to "a mixing" of the milk and that when the animal is at rest the distribution of the fat in the yield is the same as when the milk is left to stand. It was worth mentioning this paper because it shows quite clearly how modest is the experimental foundation on which the theory rests. Later verification (Borsuk and Zaks, 1955) showed that movement of the animal, especially at pasture, does not have any significant effect on the distribution of fat in a single milking.

Despite its appealing "simplicity", the creaming theory does not stand up to criticism, since both the dimensions and the relative dispositions of the alveoli and the ducts of fine calibre make it impossible that there should be any true creaming of the fat globules. The diameter of the alveoli does not exceed 0·3–0·4 mm. Therefore, the path to be followed by each globule, if creaming really occurred in the alveoli, would be measured in tens of microns, and the flow of milk to rush into the ducts at the moment of milk ejection from the hundreds of thousands of separate alveoli would undoubtedly ensure ideal intermixing of the fat. Finally, the very concepts of "upper" and "lower" are of very conditional application to the udder of the cow, with its lobe-like structure, in which the separate lobes are arranged as if in several storeys in relation to the milk passages. We would add that these concepts have even less meaning in relation to the mammary glands in the woman, in whom there is also a difference in fat content in the successive portions of the milk (Whittlestone and Perrin, 1954).

It would seem that the objections to the theory are so convincing that there is no point in returning to it now. We shall, however, see later that there is a definite connexion between the capacity of fat globules to settle and the differing fat content in successive portions of a single yield. This connexion is, however, quite different from that presupposed by the original theory of creaming.

Kirchner (1907) attempted to explain the differences in fat content in the successive portions of a milking by the separation of the fat globules by dimensions when the milk moved from the alveolar cavities to the finest calibre ducts. According to this view, the larger globules are retained in the alveoli, the liquid part of the milk being, as it were, filtered although carrying away the small globules: this leads to the accumulation of a certain amount of surplus fat in the alveolar milk, which is only removed by the energetic contractions of the alveoli in the act of milk ejection.

The morphological studies of Petersen, Palmer and Eckles (1929) have shown that no such retention of large fat globules occurs. Espe (1946) has correctly remarked that the retention of large fat globules in the alveoli would undoubtedly clog the alveolar passages. Finally this explanation loses all point after the detailed studies of Whittlestone (1954b), who has established that there is no correlation between the distribution of fat-globule size and the sequence of the portions in a single milking, or with their fat content or the period of the lactation. Whittlestone and Perrin (1954) established the same fact for human milk. It is clear that this is an insurmountable obstacle to the filtration theory. Nevertheless, we shall show later that the concept of the significance of filtration in the separation of milk by its content of fat does make some sense, although in a somewhat different way from that initially assumed.

Turner (1933, 1934) considered that the increase in the percentage of fat in successive portions of a milking was associated with the retention of fat in the alveolar cells between milkings, whilst the liquid part, which is relatively poor in fat globules, is secreted freely into the alveoli and passes into the ducts. During milking, fat is discharged from the alveolar cells and this increases its percentage content, especially in the last portions of the milk. In Turner's opinion the retention of fat is due to an increase in pressure within the alveoli when the alveolar cavities become sufficiently full, whilst the output of fat during milking is associated with the pressure drop when the alveoli are evacuated and with a simultaneous mechanical effect or, in simpler words, by expression of fat from the cells by contraction of the myoepithelium. Thus Turner reduces his explanation of this intricate act to the influence of purely mechanical factors. These considerations raise a number of doubts and do not tally with the normal physiological views on the regulation of secretion. Above all, there is no very significant rise in pressure in the storage system between milkings, especially when the udder is not very full. On the contrary, in the second stage of milk ejection, i.e., at the very moment when the milk is enriched with fat, pressure rises in the gland's storage system. It is equally unlikely that fat is expressed from the cells. This would call for the development of a force of which the myoepithelial cells are scarcely capable; moreover, an influence of this kind would scarcely be compatible with the preservation of the anatomical integrity of the secretory cells. Nevertheless, Turner's idea of the retention and accumulation of fat in the alveolar cells is a sound aspect of his theory, and one which, as we shall see below, is of fundamental significance.

Whittlestone's deliberations (1953b) are worthy of particular attention. In his view the fat globules in the alveoli undergo a specific form of aggregation ("clustering"), and whilst the formed clusters are unable to enter freely the finest calibre ducts, they do not interfere with the filtration of the liquid part of the milk, accompanied by a certain number of "free" globules, into the ducts. In the act of milk ejection the clusters of fat globules break down and milk containing an increased percentage of fat passes into the ducts and the cistern. Here we must stress the difference between Kirchner's theory of filtration and Whittlestone's view. According to Kirchner, separate globules that are so large as to be incapable of entering the opening of the outlet duct without an additional expulsive force are retained in the alveoli; according to Whittlestone, it is not separate globules, but groups or aggregates so loose that percolation of the liquid part of the milk continues without interruption, that are retained in the alveoli.

According to Whittlestone, the fat content in successive portions of a single milking varies if the milk of the given species is capable of creaming, i.e., when the fat globules can be aggregated into more compact clusters. This is, in fact, a property of human and cow's milk, which is not found, for example, in the sow, in which the fat is quite evenly distributed in all the portions of the "yield". It should be added that if the fat globules of sow's milk are added to the plasma of cow's milk they also become capable of creaming.

Thus Whittlestone's theory is an original synthesis of the theories of creaming and filtration. Whittlestone's deliberations are undoubtedly of considerable interest and go some way towards explaining the increase in fat content in the successive portions of a milking. It must be stated, however, that Whittlestone's theory is based on the assumption that the increase in fat in the successive portions follows an ascending curve and that all the milk fat is present in the storage system of the udder before milking commences. In fact, the first assumption is far from being always true and the second hardly corresponds to reality.

Borsuk and Zaks (1955) have shown that the progressive increase in the fat content of the milk in successive portions of a single milking is not an invariable occurrence. It is a typical feature of normal milkings after a sufficiently prolonged interval. When the period between milkings is shortened and also when the normal milking times are changed there is an unusual stratification, in which the fat content in the preceding portion is higher than in the subsequent portion. It even happens sometimes that the first portion of the cisternal milk contains a higher percentage of fat than the last portion to be milked out. This is shown quite clearly from an experiment on the cow Bylinka, which was remilked 2 hr. after milking (Table 10).

Borsuk (1955a) has observed various forms of the stratification of fat in successive portions in her latest experiments on milk discharge from the ducts into the cistern. Ogorodnii (1953) has also noted that under certain experimental conditions there is a slight decline in the percentage of fat in the final portion of the strippings in comparison with the preceding portion. I have observed even more striking facts of a similar kind when studying residual milk. In studies of the way in which washing the udder with hot water affects the fat content of the milk (Egorova, Zaks, Olenov, 1953) we established what was, at first sight, a somewhat improbable fact:

TABLE 10

FAT CONTENT IN SUCCESSIVE PORTIONS OF A SINGLE MILKING OF BYLINKA

	\multicolumn{3}{c}{cisternal}	\multicolumn{3}{c}{alveolar}
	1	2	3	4	5	6
Volume of portion (ml.)	50·0	50·0	50·0	50·0	250·0	250·0
Fat (%)	4·3	4·2	4·1	2·4	1·75	1·75

namely, that the fat content of the strippings was higher than that of the residual milk obtained from the animal immediately after removal of the strippings. Subsequent analysis in our laboratory revealed a number of completely new details (Olenov, 1954; Olenov and Niukkanen, 1954). In a series of successive experiments on eight cows we compared the fat content: (1) in the strippings; (2) in the residual milk; (3) in the additional portion of residual milk removed after massage; (4) in what is known as the thermal portion, which was obtained after removal of the residual milk by washing the udder with water at 56°C.; (5) in the small amount of residual milk (averaging 80 ml.) which can be milked out after removal of the thermal portion. The results of these experiments are given in Table 11.

One can see from the data in Table 11 that in the great majority of cases the fat content of the strippings is really considerably greater than that of the residual milk. The difference is 1·4% on average in favour of the strippings and it was only on a few occasions that the fat content of the strippings was the same as or only slightly greater than that of the residual milk. The difference between the residual milk and the thermal portion is even more noticeable, being 3·3% on average in favour of the thermal portion and 5% or more in some experiments. It was further found that massage after milking out the residual milk gives a similar although slightly lesser effect: the "massage" portion contains 2·4% more fat on average than does the residual milk.

The basic conclusion to be drawn is that milk with a considerably higher percentage of fat than the residual milk can be obtained from the udder by certain manipulations, and that this is possible both before and after the main quantities of the residual milk have been removed. When considering the possible physiological mechanism of the effect of these manipulations, it should be noted that stripping, massage and thermal stimuli applied to the udder

TABLE 11

FAT CONTENT (%) IN SUCCESSIVE PORTIONS OF MILK
(FROM YU. M. OLENOV)

Cow	1st—stripping after final massage	2nd—residual milk	difference between 1st and 2nd portions	3rd—additional portions of residual milk after massage	difference between 2nd and 3rd portions	4th—thermal portion of residual milk	difference between 2nd and 4th portions	5th—second portion of normal residual milk	difference between 4th and 5th portions
Acacia	9·4	9·4	0	—	—	15·0	+5·6	13·9	−1·1
	10·0	10·2	+0·2	—	—	12·8	+2·6	9·7	−3·1
	11·6	8·0	−3·6	—	—	11·4	+3·4	10·0	−1·4
	9·6	7·4	−2·2	10·8*	+3·4	14·0	+6·6	12·4	−1·6
Al'ma	10·1	7·4	−2·7	—	—	10·2	+2·8	8·6	−1·6
	—	10·6	—	14·4*	+3·8	14·6	+4·0	9·4	−5·2
Venera	9·4	9·6	+0·2	—	—	13·2	+3·6	13·0	−0·2
	—	7·2	—	—	—	12·4	+5·2	—	—
Tsapka	11·3	9·8	−1·5	12·4*	+2·6	12·8	+3·0	8·4	−4·4
	—	10·3	—	11·0**	+0·7	11·8	+1·5	7·7	−4·1
Pal'ma	—	7·1	—	8·8**	+1·7	10·4	+3·3	10·4	0
Bystraya	8·2	5·7	−2·5	—	—	6·0	+0·3	4·7	−1·3
	7·0	4·4	−2·6	—	—	6·2	+1·8	5·6	−0·6
Vernaya	—	4·6	—	—	—	5·2	+0·6	4·6	−0·6
Zvezda	6·2	6·4	+0·2	—	—	7·0	+0·6	5·7	−1·3
Average			−1·4		+2·4		+3·0***		−1·9

Note: One star denotes that after the normal residual milk had been stripped a further portion was obtained after massage followed by a thermal portion; two stars that after stripping of the normal residual milk the thermal portion was obtained before massage; three stars that in those experiments in which an additional portion of residual milk was obtained by massage that the fat content of the thermal portion exceeded that of the ordinary residual milk by 3·7% on average.

all have what is primarily a reflex effect in the first instance on the musculature of the gland's storage system, which helps to free it of the accumulated milk. This is particularly important when one bears in mind that in the conditions of the experiment, which was carried

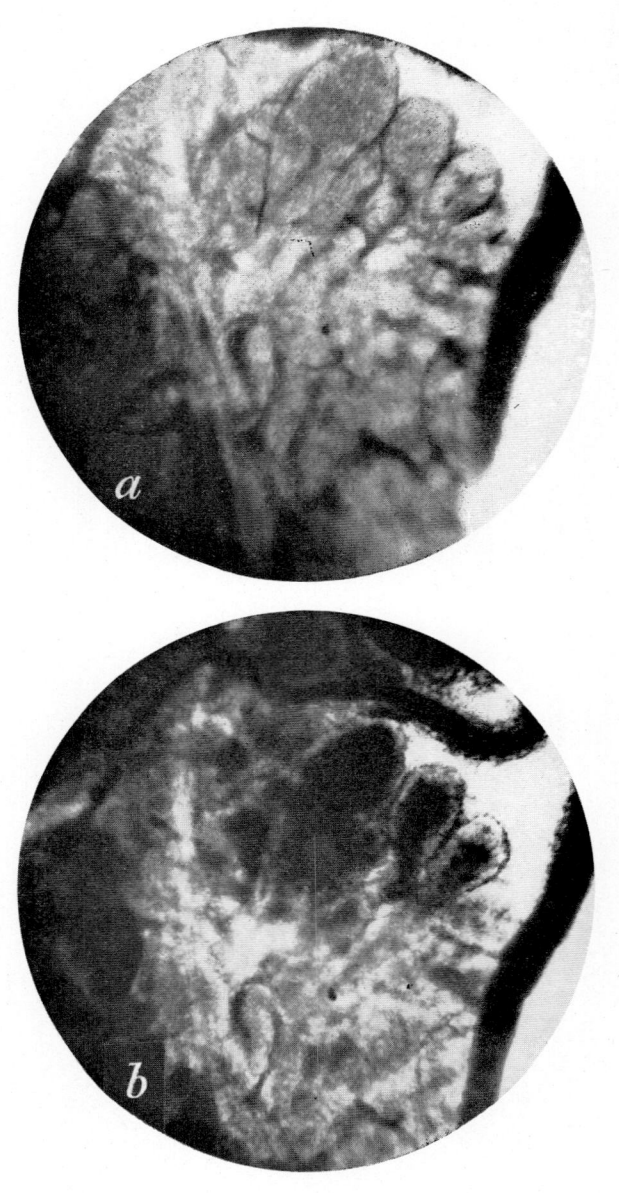

FIG. 33. Mammary gland of mouse. Evacuation of intracellular inclusions when the nerve to the gland is stimulated. (From Zotikova, 1955.)

a—before stimulation; *b*—after 15 min. stimulation by induction current.

out immediately after milking, there was little chance of obtaining a neurohumoral reflex involving the posterior pituitary.

Thus one can say that in this case reflex influences are a more effective stimulator of the removal of fat than a humoral agent—the injection of oxytocin—taken in isolation. It is also certain that there is a certain quantity of reserve milk in the udder, which contains a higher percentage of fat than the usual residual milk, and that reflex influences provide access to this milk.

Where is this fat reserve located?

It would be most natural to assume, in the light of Turner's deliberations (1933) which have already been mentioned, that this fat is to be found in the alveolar cells themselves and that its output is governed by special nervous stimuli of a secretory nature. This hypothesis is all the better founded, since we now have facts which confirm it. In this respect Zotikova's (1955) use of vital microscopy in experiments on the mammary gland of a lactating mouse is of the greatest significance. The peripheral section of the nerve running from the L_2 and L_3 roots to the given lobe of the mammary gland was stimulated with an induction current for periods of one minute separated by one-minute periods of rest. Very distinctive changes developed in the gland as a result of stimulation of the nerve. Before stimulation of the nerve commenced the lobe of the gland in a photomicrograph was optically quite uniform; fifteen minutes after commencement the secretory cells along the "periphery" of the alveoli were optically translucent. At the same time the inner contents of the alveoli (on the positive) were darkened, indicating an increase in their optical density. Stimulation did not cause any fundamental change in the dimensions and configuration of the alveoli. Consequently, the optical "thickening" of their contents is not due to a simple change in form. Zotikova's latest data show that this translucence in the cytoplasm of the epithelial cells of the alveoli is connected not with the output of fat into the lumen of the alveolus, but with migration of drops of fat to the apical ends of the cells. The movement of drops of fat into the lumen of the alveoli is stimulated by oxytocin (cited by Baryshnikov, 1960). The cells remain translucent for thirty minutes after stimulation and the effect can be repeated (Fig. 33).

A similar effect was established in rabbits in a somewhat different experiment by Pavlov and Markaryan (1955, 1957). In their experiments the young suckled only one teat. Considerable differences were revealed by histological study of the evacuated and unevacuated glands: the cells of the suckled gland contained considerably less fatty inclusions than those of the glands which had not been suckled. At the same time the alveoli of both were contracted to an almost equal degree, which showed that there was a quite strong neurohumoral reflex to the neurohypophysis. The authors conclude that, in addition to the general neurohumoral reflex, there is also a local reflex in the rabbit affecting the gland, the teat of which is stimulated by suckling. They also try to explain the fluctuations in fat content in the milk of the separate quarters of a cow's udder milked simultaneously from the same point of view.

Azimov (1955) makes a number of interesting observations on the significance of the reflex secretion of fat to the enrichment of the last portions of the milk. He concludes from data by Grynfellt, Beguchev and Glebina that there can be very considerable reserves of synthesized fat in the cytoplasm of the alveolar cells. Almost half the mass of the cell consists of fatty inclusions when the cells are most full, but this proportion apparently falls to one-sixth when the gland has been milked.

Astrakhanskaya has obtained important proof of the importance of nervous mechanisms to the discharge of milk fat from the cells (1955). She has established that denervation of the mammary gland in guinea-pigs and goats leads to considerable retention of large drops of fat in the cells of the alveoli; no marked disturbances in fat synthesis were observed, in as much as there is no fundamental decline in the total amount of fat produced by the gland after denervation and, indeed, as G. N. Pavlov (1955a) found, it may even increase under certain circumstances.

New proof of the existence of liposecretory* reflexes has been obtained in our laboratory from already mentioned (p. 84) experiments on goats with total denervation of the right half of the udder. After simultaneous complete milking of both halves of the udder the residual milk was removed by the successive use of the posterior-pituitary extract and massage in one variant and massage, posterior-pituitary extract and massage in the other. It was found that the residual milk removed from the denervated side by either combina-

* The term used by E. F. Pavlov and A. Kh. Markaryan.

tion of stimuli contained a noticeably lower percentage of fat than that obtained in the same way from the normal, control side. Table 12 shows this asymmetry quite clearly. It should also be noted that the fat content of the milk in the main yield was almost identical on the denervated and normal sides. We would also add that this asymmetry in the percentage of fat in the residual milk disappeared after procaine block of the nerves of the left (normal) gland and reappeared when the effect of the procaine had worn off.

TABLE 12

FAT CONTENT (%) IN THE MAIN MILKING AND IN THE RESIDUAL MILK IN GOATS

Goat	Left gland (normal)			Right gland (denervated)		
	milking	posterior-pituitary extract	massage	milking	posterior-pituitary extract	massage
Lipa	2·51	4·09	9·0	2·50	3·82	7·20
Marta	4·39	10·16	15·45	4·61	8·96	13·33

As indicated on p. 85, denervation of the gland did not affect its capacity to discharge residual milk: the total volumes of all portions from both the left and right halves of the udder in both goats were approximately the same. This tallies well with the hypothesis that there is a difference between the mechanisms that govern removal of the fat and the liquid part of the milk. The facts adduced are a new and quite convincing proof of the special role of nervous stimuli in the discharge of fat from the cells of the mammary gland. It is clear that if all the fat was in the storage system (alveoli and ducts) before the commencement of our manipulations, denervation could not have any particular effect on its removal, since it would not fundamentally affect the volume of residual milk removed.

In summarizing all that has been said concerning liposecretory reflexes, we ought once again to stress that in all the cases considered we are speaking of the release of previously-synthesized fat from the cytoplasm of the cells and not of an intensification in its synthesis. Nevertheless, the very mechanism of the release is associated with specific activity of the cells under the influence of the efferent nerves and not with simple mechanical expression of the fat from the cells, as was assumed by Turner.

Some confirmation of the hypothesis that secretory processes are intensified at the moment of milk ejection is provided by the data of Vladimirova (1955), who has demonstrated that there is a marked intensification (2–9-fold) in the flow of blood through the mammary gland in response to milking and that only a functioning gland reacts in this manner. Vladimirova's data may possibly be an indirect proof of the intensification of secretory processes in the act of milk ejection: it is difficult to associate the increase in blood supply with anything other than increased oxygen demand in the organ, since the motor activity of the motor elements of the udder (myoepithelium and smooth musculature), unlike secretion, can scarcely be connected with a significant rise in the expenditure of energy. It would be desirable to supplement Vladimirova's experiments by direct study of gas exchange in the gland during milk ejection.*

In the light of all that has been said, one can scarcely justify the categorical way in which Linzell (1955) denies that there is efferent innervation of the secretory cells in the mammary gland. In essence, Linzell's denial is merely based on the fact that he did not observe any secretory (or motor) effects in vital microscopy of the mammary gland of a mouse on "stimulation of the cutaneous nerves supplying the glands". The divergence between Linzell's and Zotikova's results may be due to a number of differences in their procedures (duration and other conditions of stimulation of the nerve, selection of nerve, etc.). The nature of the light source is of particular importance in the observation of liposecretory effects; Zotikova's use of transmitted light was undoubtedly superior to Linzell's incident light.

Our own facts and those of our predecessors combine to provide quite convincing material in support of the hypothesis that the release of previously-synthesized fat from the cells of the alveolar epithelium is under nervous regulation. Nevertheless, we shall run into considerable difficulties if we attempt to interpret the data in Table 10 exclusively from this point of view. The major difficulty is that the separate alveoli do not discharge directly into the cistern, but they are separated from it by an intricate system of ducts, which *in toto* comprise a storage system, which is a specific dead space. Therefore, after any manipulation which results in milk

---

* Vladimirova gives her facts a different interpretation. She regards them as a proof of the effective role of the haemodynamic factor in milk ejection.

extracted from the alveoli entering the cistern, part of the milk remains in the ducts. Naturally, it is this part which is the first to enter the cistern on subsequent manipulation, mixed with new milk, if any comes from the same alveoli. This is a regrettable interference in many lactational experiments, and one, moreover, which it is difficult to eliminate. If this circumstance is fully taken into account, the sharp leaps in fat content in successively extracted small portions of milk take on a quite special significance. In fact, the thermal portion is sometimes very small. In some experiments it is only 20–25 ml. for the whole udder and may have a 3–5% higher fat content than the residual milk just milked out. It would be highly improbable that these 20 ml. of milk could be discharged from the same alveoli and pass through the same ducts as the normal residual milk obtained two minutes before commencement of the thermal effect. A few minutes after removal of the thermal portion a little more milk (approximately 80 ml. on average for the whole udder) can be milked out. From what has been said above concerning the importance of the dead space, one could expect that the fat content of this milk would be quite close to that of the thermal portion just obtained. Even on average, however, there is a difference of 1·9% in fat content in favour of the thermal portion and in some experiments it reaches the imposing level of 5%. It is difficult to assert that this residual milk entered the cistern from the same ducts as the immediately preceding thermal portion.

Zaks, Olenov and Makeeva (1956) have obtained additional information from a study of the removal of residual milk in cows. During the study it was found that fractional portions of residual milk extracted by successive manipulations (injection of posterior-pituitary extract, milking, washing with hot water, massage, etc.) differed markedly in fat content. The nature of the fat distribution can vary greatly from experiment to experiment, especially in relation to the time at which the milk is extracted (before or immediately after milking time or between milkings). The most general and typical feature of the separate experiments is that there can be both marked increases and decreases in the fat content of small portions of milk extracted in rapid succession.

As an example, we shall make a detailed examination of the results of one such typical experiment (Fig. 34). The experiment was carried out one hour after normal milking. Preliminary milking dry by hand of the right fore quarter only yielded 100 ml. of milk (with 10·2% of fat). Subsequent injection of posterior-pituitary extract caused a further 31 ml. of milk (ppe I, ppe II, ppe III) to be discharged through a catheter, and the fat content of all three portions was considerably lower than in the milk just obtained by hand. Milking of the adjacent teats caused a relatively large quantity of milk (MI–MV) to be removed through the catheter, in which the fat content had initially declined even more than in the ppe portions, and it was only in the last sample, which was small in volume, that it increased, without, however, attaining the fat content of the milk

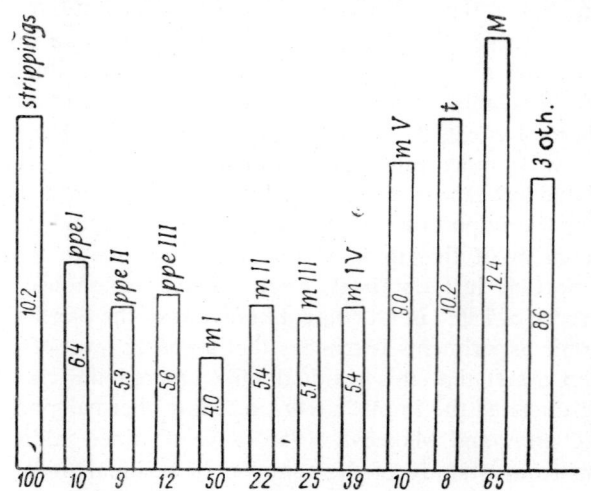

FIG. 34. Distribution of fat (%) in small successive portions of the residual milk.

Figures beneath columns—volumes of the given portions in ml. Remaining explanations in text.

obtained by milking. Then in the two following samples obtained by washing the udder with hot water (*t*) and by massage (*M*) the percentage of fat rose sharply and surpassed that of the milk obtained by milking by 2·2%. The overall fat content of all the residual milk obtained by milking the other three teats (3 oth.) after the experiment was 8·6%. When we examine these data our attention is drawn to the fact mentioned above: namely, that the portions with the highest percentage of fat were obtained by manipulations with a reflex effect (milking, massage, washing with hot water). The portions obtained by the isolated effect of a purely humoral agent—posterior-pituitary extract—were less fatty. But the existence of marked variations in fat content in either direction is even more important. If one bears in mind that sample MI, for example, was obtained ten minutes after milking, it becomes difficult or almost impossible to imagine that the strippings and MI were synthesized in the same alveoli and discharged through the same ducts.

Functional qualitative variations in the separate structural units of the mammary gland. In explanation of the facts just set out, Olenov (1954) suggested that there was a functional qualitative variation in the separate secreto-motor units of the mammary gland. The essence of his suggestion was that separate areas of the parenchyma produce milk containing different amounts of fat, and that these areas differ both in their synthetic activity and in their capacity to discharge the products of synthesis, and especially fat, into the cisterns. They do not discharge their secretions simultaneously, since there are variations in their reactivity to the stimuli that cause their evacuation. This point of view facilitates explanation of the sharp fluctuations in the fat content of small, successively extracted portions of the residual milk just described.

Olenov assumed that this qualitative variation is an attribute of the "smallest lobules" of the gland. It must be said at once that there is now very little reason to speak of the "smallest lobules": these differences are clearly associated with larger units of the gland. This viewpoint makes it easier to explain an occurrence such as the stratification of fat in the cisternal milk (Zaks and Borsuk, 1955). It becomes clear if we assume that milk, the fat content of which is subject to fluctuation, enters the cistern from the separate openings of the milk passages. The data of various authors concerning the considerable differences in fat content in separate quarters of the same udder are also of interest. As long ago as 1928 Proks pointed out that there may be a difference both in volume and in fat content of milk simultaneously milked from separate quarters of the udder. Pavlov and Markaryan (1955) observed considerable differences in the fat content of milk from separate quarters of an udder. Kobozev (1956), who used a special device to milk the quarters separately, established that the variation in fat content in the separate quarters was stable. On this basis he arrived independently at the conclusion that there could be a functional qualitative variation in separate lobes and also in smaller areas of the gland.

Aliev's data (1956) on the composition of the milk in the separate quarters of the udder of the water buffalo are of particular interest. Thus, when the milk was extracted by portions, the fat content in the milk from the left rear quarter was 3·6% in the first portion and 6·6% in the next. In corresponding samples from the left fore teat the fat content was 6·5% and 12·9%. The total output of fat was higher in the fore quarter (75 g.) than in the rear quarter (55·6 g.), although more milk was obtained from the fore quarter (1080 ml.) than from the rear (750 ml.).

In assessing the data that have been cited, one should remember that marked differences in fat content in the separate quarters may be due to the method by which the milk is obtained. This is primarily connected with a decline in the intensity of milk ejection in the course of milking and, one must suppose, especially with a decline in the liposecretory reflex. In particular, Pavlov and Markaryan interpret their results from this point of view. Nevertheless, there are a number of cases, such as the experiments of Kobozev and Aliev, in which the differences in fat content in the separate quarters are so constant that they cannot be wholly ascribed to transient variations in the conditions of evacuation. It is clear that there are deeper causes for these differences.

Kokorina (1961) conducted experiments in which special measures were employed to eliminate the effect of unevenness in milk ejection when milking the four quarters of the udder separately. The protein, lactose and fat content, all the characteristics of the fat globules, and the amount of salts were found to be the same in milk from all the quarters. Certain differences between the quarters observed in separate milkings were eliminated in the daily yield. These data do not really refute the hypothesis that there can be qualitative variation in the secretory process in the smaller secretory units within a single quarter.

One well-known confirmation of this hypothesis has been provided by Zelikovskaya (1953). She concluded from extensive histological studies of the mammary gland in cows that different types of fat secretion can be found in separate alveoli of the same udder. Purely apocrine secretion and various forms of holocrine secretion are encountered and the interrelationships of the various types of alveoli can vary in relation to the stage of the lactation and to other factors.

These data can unquestionably be linked with the concept of qualitative variation in the physiological functioning of the separate secretory units in the secretion of milk fat. Olenov (1954) has suggested that units with a higher milk fat output have certain peculiar features in their motor apparatus, that the tone of their ducts and of the sphincters that close separate groups of alveoli is relatively high, and that therefore elimination is less complete when oxytocin is the sole stimulus. Conversely, reflex influences, especially thermal influences and, to a lesser extent, massage, operate against a background of the effect of posterior-pituitary extract to open those ducts which are richest in milk fat and thus to ensure that the milk entering the cistern will have a higher fat content, on average, than the residual milk. This reasoning is confirmed by Olenov's own observations: he has established a clear correlation between the volume of residual milk obtained from the same cow on different days during an experiment and its fat content—the larger the volume, the higher the fat content (Table 13).

TABLE 13

RELATIONSHIPS BETWEEN VOLUME OF RESIDUAL MILK AND ITS FAT CONTENT
(FROM YU. M. OLENOV)

Cow	Number of experiments	Volume of residual milk, ml.	Fat in residual milk, %	Cow	Number of experiments	Volume of residual milk, ml.	Fat in residual milk, %
Acacia	3	600	7·7	Al'ma	1	700	7·4
	2	1200	9·8		2	1800	10·6
Venera	1	400	7·2	Zvezda	1	980	5·8
	1	800	9·6		1	1100	6·4
Bystraya	1	100	4·4	Tsapka	1	250	9·8
	1	500	5·7		1	800	10·3

The figures in Table 13 show that the total fat content of residual milk is dependent on the strength of the alveolar contraction as well as on the patency of the various ducts: more powerful contraction of the alveoli (which is naturally assumed when the volume of residual milk obtained from the same animal increases) better overcomes the resistance of the ducts.

In Olenov's experiments the normal periods between milkings were deliberately not varied. Unforeseen changes in the periods have a different effect on the volume and fat content of residual milk. Turner (1955b) found that when the period between milking was increased from 10–14 hr. to 24 hr. and above, the volume of the residual milk declined from 17·8 to 13·9% of the total volume of a single milking and that there was a slight increase in the fat content of the residual milk.

In our laboratory, recent findings by Egorova suggest that there are differences in the chemical composition of the fat in successive portions of a single milking. The iodine number of the fat is lower in the portions rich in fat than in those of low fat content. This fact remains highly consistent in different variants of the experiments and there are cases in which the divergence between the figures for the iodine number in the successive portions of a single milking are even greater than the considerable difference in fat content between the first and last portions. This can be seen, for example, when comparing cows of different breeds with a different level of milk fat. In East Friesians with a 5·26% difference in fat content between the first and last portions, the divergence in iodine number in these portions was 0·34 of a unit; the corresponding figures for brown Latvian cattle were 6·7% and 1·02.

In addition to helping to evacuate the udder completely and increasing the fat content in the last portions of the milk, increase in the intensity of milk ejection also led to greater divergence between the iodine number in the first and last portions. Egorova obtained a similar result from experiments in which washing the udder with hot water was the stimulus for milk ejection. In the control period, when the udder was washed before milking with water at a temperature of 30–30°C., the difference in fat content between the first and last portions was only 3·9% (1·5% in the first and 5·4% in the last) and the difference in iodine number was 0·72 of a unit. In the experimental period, when the udder was washed with water at 53°C., the fat difference rose to 4·85% and the iodine number difference to 1·30 of a unit.*

This feature was even more clearly revealed in experiments in which successive fractional portions of the residual milk were

---

* These figures are averaged indices for four cows and each period of the experiment lasted for three weeks.

removed. Here Egorova used the same method for obtaining the residual milk as had been used by Zaks, Olenov and Makeeva (1956). I give one example (Table 14).

In relation to fat content, therefore, Egorova's data were in complete agreement with the earlier findings of our laboratory. A new feature that was clearly revealed was that undulatory fluctuations in the percentage of fat were matched by similar variations in the iodine number in the opposite direction. This can be seen more clearly in the diagram (Fig. 35) drawn from the figures in Table 14. No evident correlation was discovered between casein content and the percentage of fat: the almost regular decline in the percentage of casein between the first and last portions is independent of variations in the fat content of the milk. I shall return to this point a little later.

TABLE 14

FAT CONTENT, IODINE NUMBER AND CASEIN CONTENT IN SUCCESSIVE PORTIONS OF THE RESIDUAL MILK OF AL'MA
(AVERAGED DATA FROM 5 EXPERIMENTS)

Nature of influence	Fat, %	Iodine Number	Casein, %
Stripping (before injection of posterior-pituitary extract)	11·2	35·42	2·23
Post. pit. extr. I.	8·7	36·17	2·20
Post. pit. extr. II	9·2	36·22	2·20
Post. pit. extr. III	9·3	36·14	2·22
Milking of adjacent teats	13·4	35·04	2·15
Milking of adjacent teats	13·8	35·00	2·14
Washing with water at 56°C.	15·7	34·16	2·10
Udder massage	15·5	34·10	2·13

One may therefore take it as established that there is a qualitative variation in the content of unsaturated fatty acids in milk fat. It is important to note that this is not an isolated and exceptional occurrence, but a regular feature in animals of different breeds, at different stages in the lactation, fed in different ways and subject to other variations.

The following hypotheses provide possible explanations of this fact: either the difference arises when the milk fat is synthesized in the cells of the secretory epithelium, or chemical reorganization of the fat takes place at a later state, in the storage system, after secretion from the cells. The second assumption is not very likely, since it is difficult to conceive of such energetic enzymic processes (without which such reorganization would scarcely be possible) taking place outside the cytoplasm. In any case, although the enzymic composition of milk has been studied in a fair amount of detail, no one has as yet detected enzymes which would make this reorganization possible. The assumption becomes even more improbable when one

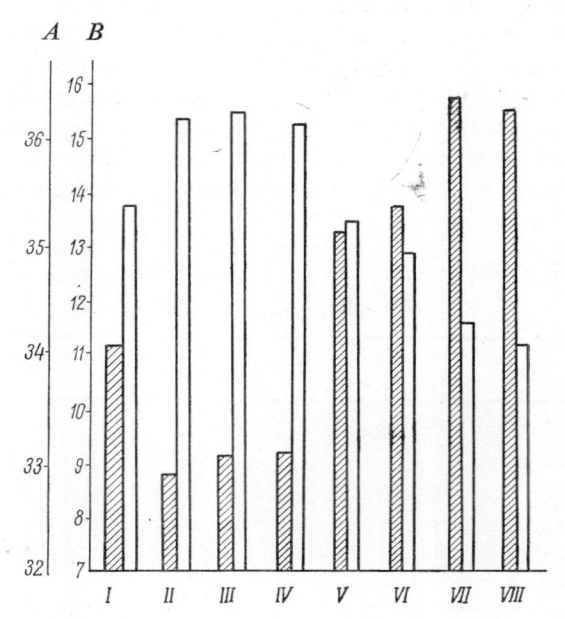

FIG. 35. Iodine number (unshaded columns) and fat content (shaded columns) in successive portions of residual milk.

I—stripping; *II–IV*—portions obtained with posterior-pituitary extract; *V*, *VI*—samples obtained when milking adjacent teats; *VII*—washing with water at 56°C.; *VIII*—udder massage. *A*—iodine number; *B*—fat, %.

bears in mind that the greatest difference in quality is found in small portions of residual milk removed in rapid succession. If one accepts the first hypothesis that the features of the chemical composition of the fat are established during its synthesis one is forced inescapably to a further conclusion: namely, that fat of different composition is formed in different secretory units of the mammary gland. If this were not so and if the same alveoli synthesized fat of differing composition in the period between milkings, the fat globules would undoubtedly be so completely mixed when the secretion was discharged into the alveoli, especially during milk ejection, that the differences established by Egorov would be completely masked and could not be detected by the methods used.

It can, therefore, be said that Egorov's facts are a most important confirmation of the hypothesis set out above that there is functional qualitative variation in the separate units of the mammary gland.

Factors that condition differences in fat content in successive portions of the yield. It is obvious that this hypothesis (and it is a hypothesis and not a theory) cannot claim to be the only explanation for differences in fat content in successive portions of a milking, and, even more, that it cannot fully explain the mechanism of fat removal. What follows is once again a highly tentative and schematic outline of the overall causes of the development of differences in fat content in the successive portions of the yield and of the way in which the removal of fat is stepped up during milking.

Immediately after milking, the dead space—the ducts—is filled with the relatively fatty residual milk. Newly secreted milk continues to enter the alveoli at this time. In the process of secretion a certain, probably quite large, part of the fat synthesized is retained and accumulates in the cells. The fat globules which enter the alveolar cavities with the milk plasma are partially aggregated (Whittlestone) and retained in the alveolar cavities, whilst the liquid part of the milk, which is low in fat, is gradually filtered into the ducts, where it dilutes the milk of relatively high fat content that is already present in them. This is why the first portion can be fattier than the next portion when a cow is remilked within 1–3 hr. of milking (Borsuk and Zaks, 1955).

When milk begins to enter the cistern freely it is already quite dilute and the cistern is filled with milk that is relatively watery. There is some decline in the rate of fat synthesis at this time (Nikitin *et al.*, 1953). Throughout this period those units of the gland that produce most fat discharge less into the cisterns than units secreting low-fat milk, and the cisternal milk is even further diluted.

During milking the milk is enriched with fat in the following ways:

(1) when the alveoli contract the fat globules that have been

aggregated in the alveolar cavities disintegrate (are agitated) and are forced into the ducts and then into the cistern;

(2) the ducts, including some from lobules producing a high quantity of milk fat, open as a result of reflex stimuli associated with massage, washing and stimulation of the teats during milking, etc., and this facilitates the movement of the fat present in the alveolar cavities;

(3) the corresponding stimuli give rise to liposecretory reflexes, under the influence of which there is an additional influx of fat accumulated in the secretory cells into the storage system.

It is, of course, difficult at present to say exactly what fraction of the milk fat discharged in a single milking is removed in this latter manner. Azimov's data (1955) on the amount of fatty inclusions only indicate that there is a considerable reserve of synthesized fat in the secretory cells. It is possible that results obtained by Petersen, Palmer and Eckles (1929) when analysing yields from an udder amputated immediately after milking may be of significance for an approximate calculation. The experiment was carried out with a cow in which the functional characteristics of both halves of the udder were almost identical, both in yield and in the composition of the milk (percentage of fat, dry matter, lactose, ash, etc.). The right half of the udder was completely emptied of milk just before the animal was slaughtered and the left half after slaughtering. The volume of the "posthumous" milk was slightly higher than from the right half, evidently owing to the exudation of certain quantities of tissue fluid into the alveoli and ducts. But the content and distribution of the fat in the milk was subject to great variations: the percentage of fat declined to 2·41 (instead of 3·78) and the total amount fell from 63·74 to 52·32 g. Whereas there had been a typical increase in fat content in the successive portions when the animal was alive, it was uniform in all except one of the portions after slaughtering: during life—1st portion 1240 g. (2·1% fat). 2nd—539 g. (6·1%), 3rd—67 g. (7·2%); posthumous—1st portion 415 g. (2% fat), 2nd—393 g. (2%), 3rd—377 g. (2·2%), 4th —394 g. (2·3%), 5th—285 g. (4·2%), 6th—311 g. (2·9%). All secretory reflexes are excluded in posthumous milk removal and forced mechanical influences can only extract the milk present in the storage system. It is therefore natural to assume that the fat deficiency in posthumous milking (approximately 21% of total output when alive) was at the expense of fatty intracellular inclusions normally discharged as a result of liposecretory reflexes. The increase in fat content in the fifth posthumous portion was probably associated with the output of part of the fat aggregated in the alveoli.

I think it highly probable that, as suggested by Azimov (1955), the reflexes which condition the release of fat in response to milking are subject to some time lag and even develop towards the end of milking and possibly even after it has finished. It is true that it is difficult to say whether the delay in the transfer of fat into the ducts and cistern is exclusively due to the time lag in the liposecretory reflex, or whether it is to some extent dependent on resistance in the duct system and especially in the ducts of the lobules that produce a high quantity of milk fat.

It is thus apparent that two main processes can be distinguished in the release of milk fat from the cells into the storage system of the udder; continuous release, that maintains an almost constant and invariable level from milking to milking, and abrupt release, that mainly occurs during milking. Continuous release is mainly determined by conditions that develop within the secretory cells; it is subordinated to humoral stimuli and the regulatory role of the nervous system is here minimal. At all events, continuous release of fat does not suffer noticeably when one of the glands is denervated if the nervous connexions of the other gland are not interrupted.

Abrupt release is quite another matter. Here the influence of direct nervous impulses is most clearly expressed and one can say that the whole process is subordinated to it.

In the light of what has been said, there can be the following causes for the retention of fat during milking when the yield is not subject to significant variation: (1) the inhibition, weakening or retardation of the liposecretory reflexes; (2) incomplete evacuation of the glandular areas in which fat production is highest; (3) weakening in the contraction of the alveoli, leading to the retention in their cavities of part of the aggregated fat if the reflex to the neurohypophysis is weak or inhibited. In the latter case there will be a more considerable decline in the amount of milk removed.

Certain qualifications must, of course, be made to this outline. In the first place, the discharge of milk fat, whatever the mechanisms that govern it may be, is the result of processes of synthesis, which provide the basis and background for the discharge of fat from the gland. Furthermore, most of the facts that have been cited can be given a completely different interpretation on the assumptions: (1) that milk fat formed in the alveoli is diluted during its subsequent progress through the ducts owing to an additional secretion of the liquid part of the milk; (2) that the relatively liquid "initial" milk is condensed and concentrated after synthesis by selective reabsorption of part of the water and water-soluble substances in the storage system. Although the first assumption is purely hypothetical, there are observations concerning the existence of a vigorous exchange between the blood and the milk (Azimov, 1955), after the milk has entered the storage system, which support the second assumption. Only further detailed study will reveal the true significance of these processes in milk synthesis and in varying the composition of the successive portions.

Sineshchekov (1956a, 1956b) has recently formulated a new theory which attempts to explain the difference in fat content in separate fractions of a single yield in a completely different way.

Sineshchekov explains differences in the composition of the various fractions by stating that milk rich in fat and other organic constituents, especially protein, is synthesized in the alveoli, whilst the liquid fraction, low in fat and protein, is mainly formed in the udder cisterns. "I consider," he writes, "that the chemical and biological features of the milk of the first and second fractions are determined by the fact that the different fractions are formed in different zones of the cow's udder, without excluding the partial movement of milk between milking from the upper zone into the area of the lower zone. My hypothesis that the different fractions of the milk originate in different zones is based on Academician I. P. Pavlov's theory of the origin of the varying composition of gastric juice." He then gives an account of the differing structure and function of the glands of different parts of the stomach and concludes that different zones of the mammary gland also have different significance for the secretion of milk. In Sineshchekov's opinion, the glands in the folds of the mucous membrane of the milk cistern may be responsible for the formation of considerable quantities of the milk in the first fraction. The cistern is thus a "gigantic alveolus", that is completely unlike the alveoli in the upper part of the mammary gland.

Thus, Sineshchekov's main argument is based on analogies between the mammary gland and the mucous membrane of the stomach. Analogy is, however, sometimes an artificial approach. It is true that larger nodules of secretory tissue are sometimes found in the walls of the udder and teat cistern in addition to a few small glands, and that these have been found (Rikhter, 1939) to be an organic defect in a dairy cow that hampers hand and especially machine milking, but this is the exception rather than the rule—an anatomical anomaly and not a normal feature. Even in these cases the reference is to glandular areas, the structure of which does not differ fundamentally from that of the main glandular parenchyma of the udder. There is no basis for assuming that the cistern contains a highly-developed glandular apparatus capable of secreting considerable volumes of milk. We have already indicated that when there is a considerable period between milkings the "first fraction" (the cisternal portion) is the major part of the yield. Proofs more closely supported by facts than simple analogy with the secretion of gastric juice are required to convince one that all this milk, or even a considerable part of it, has been formed in the cistern. This viewpoint fails to explain many of the facts cited above, such as the stratification of fatty and liquid portions of milk in the cisternal fraction, cases in which the cisternal milk contains more fat than the alveolar milk (when the period between milkings is shortened), etc. I would also add that there are considerable variations in the fat content of successive portions in species of mammal in which the cistern of the mammary gland is absent or poorly developed. Thus, Aliev (1956) found that there was a clearly defined difference between the fat content of the successive portions of the yield in water buffaloes, although there is no cisternal portion and no milk is discharged when the cistern is catheterized, however full the udder may be. There is also clear demarcation between the fat content of the successive portions in the woman, although she does not have a cistern. A secretory role could, of course, be ascribed to the mucous membrane of the milk sinuses, but there is no glandular tissue in the walls of the milk sinuses in the woman that could secrete even watery milk. It is also difficult to accept the assertion that there is less protein in the cisternal than in the alveolar milk. Unfortunately, the author fails to give any figures or other facts to support this assertion, which does not tally with existing information on the protein content of successive fractions of the yield.

I am therefore forced to the conclusion that Sineshchekov's theory is, as yet, unsupported by any facts that would lead me to accept it. Nevertheless, a sound aspect of the theory is that it admits of qualitative variation in the secretory process in different parts of the udder.

The distribution of casein and other substances in successive portions of the yield. Very little is known about the way in which the other substances in milk are distributed in the successive portions of a single milking or about the manner of their discharge. It is generally considered that fat is an exception and that casein, lactose, salts and other substances are evenly distributed in the successive portions (Espe, 1946; Petersen, 1950), although this opinion is advanced without reference to facts which could support it. The basis exists for further study of this question.

TABLE 15

FAT AND CASEIN CONTENT IN SUCCESSIVE PORTIONS OF A SINGLE MILKING IN COWS (FROM BORSUK AND ZAKS)

Cow	No. and name of sample	Volume of sample, ml.	Fat %	Casein %
Osetrina	1. cisternal	500	2·75	3·34
	2. ,,	430	3·80	3·73
	3. alveolar	250	4·40	3·82
	4. ,,	100	6·20	4·10
Shelukha	1. cisternal	250	1·50	2·86
	2. ,,	250	1·25	3·25
	3. ,,	250	2·10	3·38
	4. alveolar	250	4·05	3·11
	5. ,,	100	4·40	2·88
Zhestokaya	1. cisternal	250	1·40	3·20
	2. ,,	200	2·90	2·83
	3. ,,	250	3·15	2·78
	4. alveolar	50	2·20	2·87
	5. ,,	100	5·40	2·67

Schmidt-Mülheim (1883) was apparently the first to note that the first and last portions of milk differ in their content of casein as well as of milk fat, but his data have still not been verified and have, in fact, been forgotten. According to Ogorodnii (1953), other constituents of the milk, in addition to fat, vary their ratios in successive portions of the yield. This applies in particular to citric acid and its salts.

Borsuk and Zaks (1955) have established that casein content is subject to definite variations in successive portions, but that these changes are not as regular as in the case of fat. I cite figures from an experiment on three cows as an example of these changes (Table 15).

The figures in Table 15 show that changes in casein content in successive portions of a single yield do not follow those of fat. Apart from the fact that there is a much wider range of variation in the amount of fat, the direction of the fluctuations is usually different in the two substances. One's attention is also drawn to the fact that there is considerable variation in the nature of fluctuations in casein in different cows. In general, however, there is a tendency for casein to decline in the last portions, i.e., in those portions which are richest in fat. Table 15 contains typical examples.

Facts that accord closely with what has been said have been established in our laboratory by A. A. Egorova. She was also unable to discover any clear relationship between fat and casein content in successive portions of a yield, and the percentage of casein showed a tendency to fall in the alveolar portions. The figures in Table 14 are a very clear illustration of the view that there is no direct correlation between the content of fat and casein. According to Egorova, variations in casein content may be revealed either as undulatory fluctuations or as a progressive decline.

It can be shown that these facts apparently contradict the data of Inikhov (1951), Shvabe (1949) and other authors, who assert that there is a definite positive correlation between the content of fat and casein in milk and that milk with a high fat content also contains a high percentage of casein. This leads to the major conclusion that the secretion of both substances is in some way linked. The contradiction is, however, only apparent, since we are dealing with completely different conditions for the taking of samples. The authors cited studied the fat:casein ratio in the total yields of different cows, whereas we compared these ratios in the successive portions of a single milking in the same cows. Thus our data are a further confirmation of the hypothesis already advanced, that fluctuations in fat content in the separate portions of a yield are more conditioned by the nature of the discharge of fat that is already synthesized then by changes in its rate of synthesis.

Data contained in a new paper by Shvabe (1956) are of great importance for further study of fluctuations in the separate constituents of milk in successive portions of a single milking. In the first place, he has established that the nature of fat distribution in a single milking is dependent on the stage of the lactation, and that retention of fat in the last portions is more marked at the beginning of lactation and in its first half. This gives rise to the practical demand that stripping should be particularly thorough and that milking should be speeded up in the first half of the lactation. Furthermore, Shvabe follows his predecessors in concluding that the content of protein, sugar and (as he has been the first to establish) mineral substances declines in the successive portions. It is true that, in his opinion, this decline is largely eliminated if the calculations are made on the basis of the content of these substances in fat-free milk, but the decline in these indices is retained in relation to residual milk even when the figures are converted to a fat-free basis.

This qualification does not, in general, prevent the author from accepting our opinion that there is no rigorous connexion between the secretion of fat and protein: ". . . intensified secretion of fat is not accompanied by simultaneous intensified secretion of protein and lactose, but more likely by the reverse."

It should be added that re-examination of the view that there is a close link between the synthesis of milk fat and casein is also made necessary by Kleiber's studies (1954). He has shown that when ^{14}C-labelled precursors are injected into the blood of dairy cows, the greatest specific activity (content of the radioisotope) is observed in the casein and lactose in the 3 hr. after injection, but in the milk fat only after 7 hr.

Egorova's data show that lactose is the most stable component of milk: only occasionally is there some slight increase in its content in successive portions of the yield.

CHAPTER FOUR

THE RELATIONSHIPS BETWEEN MILK REMOVAL AND SYNTHESIS

A detailed exposition of the secretion of milk does not come within the scope of this book, but we must consider the extent to which periodic evacuations of the gland's storage system at the time of milk ejection and periodic changes in conditions in the storage system as it fills between milkings affect the secretory activity of the mammary gland.

These questions are of the greatest practical importance. It is only from a detailed study of the relationship between the evacuation of the mammary gland and its secretion that we can provide a solid foundation for the development of correct milking procedures and, in particular, that we can decide on the most rational frequency of milking.

The effect on milk secretion of the completeness with which the gland is emptied. It is widely held that incomplete milking, in which a considerable part of the milk is left in the storage system, has an unfavourable effect on milk synthesis and leads, in the last analysis, to termination of the lactation. This opinion is firmly supported by the whole practice of dairy farming: it is thought that continual undermilking causes greater harm than, for example, a reduction in the frequency of milking and extension of the interval between milkings. Shaumyan (1955) commented with every reason that the intensity of milking is governed more by the quality of milking than by its frequency, and the completeness of milking out is certainly a fundamental criterion of the quality of milking.*

---

* The desire for complete milking out should not, of course, be pursued to the extent of prolonging the milking time. In this case economic requirements would be sacrificed to physiology, which would be incorrect, since the main problem in dairy farming is not to obtain milk at any price, but to

The importance to milk synthesis of the completeness with which the udder is emptied is, in itself, scarcely open to doubt, but we still know very little about the physiological causes for the effect which evacuation of the storage system has on the secretory activity of the mammary gland. We can only make the following conjectures as to the possible mechanisms of this interrelationship.

1. Milking out is complete when milking is intensive and correctly carried out, and correct milking is in itself a vigorous activator of the secretory process, owing to reflex stimulation of the adenohypophysis from the exteroceptors of the teats and udder. The efferent fibres of the udder may also be involved in activation. I have already indicated the significance of this latter factor in, for example, the discharge of fat from the cells.

2. The act of milk ejection is accompanied by a number of rapidly developing changes in conditions within the storage system: an increase in pressure, followed by a decrease, an intricate motor reaction of the alveoli, ducts and cisterns, sharp fluctuations in the supply of blood to the gland and in the chemical composition of the secretion which fills each given section of the storage system, and, finally, variation in the chemical nature of the secretory cells themselves. The intensity of these changes is directly proportional to the completeness and speed of evacuation of the udder at milking time. It is certain that the occurrence of all these events in such a short space of time within the storage system will activate the corresponding interoceptors in its walls. A number of similar changes take place in the storage system as it fills between milkings although at a much slower rate than in the act of milk ejection. All these intricate stimuli from the interoceptors maintain the reflex secretory process.

3. The effect of milk ejection on secretion is governed by purely local processes, by a change in conditions that arises when the cells and associated storage spaces are freed of the secretion. This factor is, however, probably less important, since what are known as

increase milk production whilst reducing costs, especially labour costs. Nevertheless, a knowledge of the physiological features of milk ejection makes it possible to milk a cow as completely as possible and yet to reduce and not extend milking time. This can be done by correct preparation of the animal for milking and the most rational use of time when the animal is ready to give milk. This will be examined in detail in the next chapter.

local regulations cannot be separated *in vivo* from nervous and neurohumoral regulations.

In general terms one can say that removal of the secretion is an important condition for the optimum activity of any exocrine gland and that the mammary gland is no exception to this rule. There are two main questions for detailed examination in any analysis of the interrelationships of the processes of milk removal and secretion: (1) which impulses from the storage system that develop as it fills and is emptied are most important to the maintenance of milk secretion; (2) how does the rate and completeness with which the secretion is evacuated from the gland affect the secretory process?

Tverskoi (1953) has made detailed studies of the first question in goats. He was able to establish that impulses from the storage system play such an effective part that they can maintain secretion even when the stimuli associated with milking are totally excluded. The goats were not milked for 16–19 days, but the cistern was freed of milk twice a day by catheterization or (in another set of experiments) by permanent fistulas (catheters inserted in the openings of the teats and closed by screw caps). The alveolar milk was also removed twice a day by the injection of posterior-pituitary extract. Under these conditions there was even a slight increase in yield by comparison with the control days. Nor did yields fall when the conditions under which the animals were kept, i.e. the whole pattern associated with the experiment, were deliberately and greatly altered so as to exclude the possible influence of temporary connexions developed by the animal to the conditions of milking. It was further shown that when the cisterns were continually drained through permanent catheters (the milk was accumulated in special collectors) secretion was maintained at a relatively constant level if the alveolar section was freed of its contents twice a day by the injection of posterior-pituitary extract. Thus, the cessation of pressure fluctuations in the cistern did not affect the secretory process. When the injections of posterior-pituitary extract were stopped in the subsequent course of the experiment, there was a rapid decline in milk secretion; although the extent of the decline varied considerably in different animals, in no one of the five animals did it cease entirely even after the experiment had been in progress for 10–25 days, but was established at a new and lowered, but stable level.

When injections of posterior-pituitary extract were resumed secretion recovered, although it did not, for various reasons, regain the initial level in all the goats. When the injections of posterior-pituitary extract were discontinued the production of milk fat declined even more than the yields.

The main conclusion to be drawn from Tverskoi's experiments is that periodic evacuation of the alveolar section is most important if the level of secretion, especially of milk fat, is to be maintained. It is difficult, of course, to say whether the decline in secretion in this case was exclusively associated with interruptions in pressure fluctuations or whether it was caused by the considerable disturbance to other conditions, especially disturbance to the chemical nature of the cells associated with the retention of fat. Another important conclusion is that even such a sharp disturbance of physiological conditions did not terminate secretion, but only reduced its level. This does not, of course, show that the afferent impulses from the udder that occur when the animal is milked in the normal way are not of fundamental significance; what it does prove is that the secretion of milk is maintained not by one but by several mechanisms, and that when one of them declines or is interrupted its role is fulfilled, in whole or in part, by the others.

Tverskoi gave an even clearer example of this "multiple maintenance" in his later experiments (1955a). He showed that milk secretion in goats can be maintained at nearly the initial level for a long time after total denervation of the whole udder or after transections of the spinal cord, i.e., when all possibility of afferent signals from the gland had been excluded. It was only necessary to evacuate the udder periodically by milking and injections of posterior-pituitary extract; even stopping the injections did not terminate, but only reduced, secretion. Tverskoi's findings here tally with those of Goltz and Ewald (1896) and Popov (1950), who were able to observe lactation in dogs whose spinal cord had been severed or extirpated. It is, however, outside the scope of this book to consider the possible ways in which milk secretion is maintained under these conditions.

Tverskoi's findings undoubtedly show that periodic evacuation of milk from the alveolar section is of importance to secretion. Nevertheless, he establishes this fact in a general way and does not go into details, since this would have been outside his purpose. The effect of the rate and completeness of evacuation, or of greatly forced evacuation of the secretion, etc., is, however, of fundamental theoretical and practical importance.

In one paper by Tverskoi (1953) it is indicated that there was even a slight increase in yield on repeated injection of posterior-pituitary extract although milking manipulations were discontinued. The completeness of evacuation of the alveoli alone increased the effectiveness of secretion. These facts confirm the earlier results of Knodt and Petersen (1944) obtained from five cows which were injected with "Pitocin" at every milking for 14 days. There was an increase in yield and in the total production of milk fat, although the experiments were conducted in the second half of the lactation, when the lactation curve was falling. It was also noted that there was a gradual decline in the amount of milk given by the cow in the main milking during the period of the experiment and simultaneous increase in the volume of the "Pitocin milk". It is apparent that the exogenous hormone inhibited the activity of the animal's own neurohypophysis or reduced the effectiveness of the natural milk-ejection reflex in some other manner. This detail from the experiment by Knodt and Petersen is of extreme fundamental interest and should certainly attract attention.

Adams and Allen (1952) have concluded from similar experiments that the injection of oxytocin at every milking increases the total output of milk fat by a certain increase in yield whilst the average percentage of fat remains more or less unchanged. Sprain, Smith, Tyler and Fosgate (1954) have traced the effect of oxytocin injected during alternate 14-day periods throughout the whole of a lactation in seven cows. This prolonged experiment also confirmed the main conclusion of Adams and Allen. Thus, intentionally forced evacuation of the alveoli led to some intensification in the gland's secretory activity.

Donker, Koshi and Petersen (1954) injected a cow daily for 70 days with 1–3 i.u. of oxytocin given intravenously. They also reported a considerable increase in yield and in the output of milk fat. They concluded that the mechanism of this aspect of the action of oxytocin was unknown, but was clearly associated with more than the evacuation of the gland. This is, of course, only a supposition. At all events, I have not found any indications in the available foreign literature that oxytocin has a specifically lactogenic effect.

Tverskoi has shown that the Soviet preparations of posterior-pituitary extract are also without a lactogenic action (from their effect on the crop gland of the pigeon).*

Intensified complete extraction of milk by normal milking methods, i.e. under more physiological conditions, leads to the same results. I shall refrain from giving an account of the extensive literature in animal husbandry in which there are copious references to the fact that complete removal of the milk, however it may be achieved (by the optimum rate of milking, the correct sequence in milking the quarters, deft combination of milking and massage, etc.), invariably increases the yield and the percentage of fat in a given milking, and, when regularly achieved, also leads to an increase in yield and in the overall production of milk fat. I shall only mention the review article by Solov'ev (1952), in which a proper account of this literature is given. It is true that the authors of some studies hold a somewhat different opinion. Thus, for example, Woodward, Hotis and Graves (1936) have concluded from lengthy observations that the decline in the milk production of cows that are incompletely milked is only slightly more than 3% of the yield of the same cows when completely milked. Woodward *et al.* found that incomplete milking did not have any significant effect on the average percentage of fat for the lactation. Nevertheless, one can fully agree with Espe (1946) that incomplete milking can only have as slight an effect as this when the amount of milk left in the udder is not in excess of 400 ml., and that more incomplete milking can have a negative effect on the animal's productivity.

I shall dwell on certain studies in which the mechanism of the effect of the separate approaches to stepping up the evacuation of milk during milking was subjected to more detailed physiological

---

* Benson and Folley have, however, recently presented new data (1956) which have an important bearing on the assessment of the results of experiments in which posterior-pituitary extract is injected during lactation. They have shown that if the young are removed from rats on the fourth day, daily injection of 1 i.u. of oxytocin prevents the involution of the mammary glands that normally develops very rapidly after suckling has ceased. They cite Bradley in exclusion of the possibility that oxytocin has a direct effect on the secretion of the mammary gland; in the given case its effect is connected with stimulation of the lactogenic function of the anterior pituitary. It is evident that oxytocin can intensify the secretion of the mammary gland, and not only by freeing it more completely from its secretion.

analysis. Thus, we have made in our laboratory a detailed study of the effect of washing the udder with hot water before milking. These studies and those of other laboratories have shown, as has the use of the method under normal farming conditions, that its regular use brings about a considerable increase in the output of milk fat, of the order of 2·5 kg. per metric ton of milk obtained.

Washing the udder with hot water is effective when it is first employed. Olenov and Niukkanen (1954) found that when the udders of four cows were first washed with hot water at the 10-o'clock milking, the increase in fat content considerably exceeded both the average and the maximum percentage of fat from the same cows for a 10-day control period. We would recall that the essence of the thermal stimulus is to be found in the responding reaction of the ducts, as a result of which a certain additional quantity of milk with a high fat content enters the cistern. It is now important to pay attention to another aspect of the matter: namely, that the regular

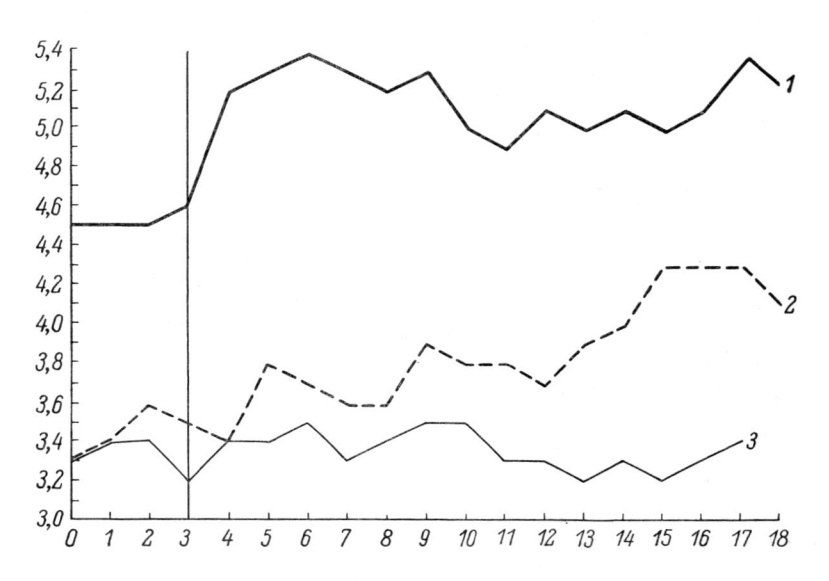

FIG. 36. Increase in fat content with systematic daily washing of the udder with hot water at milking time.

1—Acacia; *2*—Belyanka; *3*—Zvezda. *X-axis*—duration of experiment (days); *y-axis*—fat (%). The line parallel to the y-axis marks the beginning of washing the udder with hot water.

extraction of excess fat by the use of the thermal stimulus increases production, i.e., increases the synthesis of fat.

It can be seen from Fig. 36 that the stimulation of fat synthesis is manifest in quite different ways in different cows. There was an immediate increase in the percentage of fat given by the cow Acacia, which was maintained, with light fluctuations, at the new increased level. This is an example of an animal that reacts quickly to increased evacuation of fat from the udder. Belyanka reacts more slowly and only reaches her maximum when the udder has been washed with hot water for 15 days. This is an example of an animal in which the fat-synthesizing function of the mammary gland is slow to change. Finally, Zvezda failed to react at all to thermal stimuli. Approximately 20–25% of the large number of cows which we have examined were of this type.

These cows were a very suitable subject for clarification of some of the mechanisms that make the mammary gland able to react by an increased rate of synthesis to forced evacuation of milk and milk fat from the udder.

TABLE 16
INDIVIDUAL FEATURES OF THE REACTION OF COWS TO ONCE ONLY AND SYSTEMATIC WASHING OF THE UDDER WITH HOT WATER
(FROM YU. M. OLENOV AND L. A. NIUKANNEN)

Cow	Change in fat content of a single milking (%) when udder washed once only in hot water by comparison with:		Change in fat content in strippings (%) when udder washed once only in hot water by comparison with:		Changes in fat content (%) after prolonged washings in hot water
	average fat content in preparatory period	maximum fat content in preparatory period	average fat content in preparatory period	maximum fat content in preparatory period	
Al'ma	+0·8	+0·1	+3·1	+10·4	+0·3
Molniya	+0·4	+0·2	—	—	0
Tsapka	0	−0·4	+2·2	+0·9	0
Zvezda	0	−0·1	+0·1	−0·3	0

Olenov has shown that cows that do not react to regular washing of the udder with hot water can be classified by the way in which they respond to the first "unexpected" washing with hot water. Typical examples of these differences are compared in Table 16 with one of the cows that responded positively both to a single treatment and to regular washing of the udder with hot water.

The basis selected for comparison was the increase in the fat percentage when hot washing was first employed, in the whole yield and in its last portions (the strippings). These increments were compared with the average and maximum fat content of the milk in the preparatory period before the use of hot washing.

Al'ma gave an immediate increase in fat content and this increase was well maintained when the udder was washed regularly with hot water. The first treatment increased the fat content of the milk throughout the yield and especially in the strippings. Al'ma therefore had a plentiful and fairly mobile reserve of fat in the udder; removal of this reserve stimulated the fat-synthesizing function of the gland.

Systematic application of heat failed to produce any increase in the fat content of the milk in the next three cows. The reasons for this were clearly different. The fat content of the yield from Molniya was considerably increased by the first treatment: she had a plentiful and fairly mobile fat reserve, but its removal did not stimulate synthesis. Tsapka's reaction to the first application of the stimulus was weak: fat content was only increased in the strippings after massage, and even so considerably less than in Al'ma. Apparently the reserve that could be obtained from Tsapka by a thermal stimulus was slight. Finally, Zvezda failed completely to react to the first hot washing. Cows of this type clearly do not have a sufficiently mobile fat reserve in the udder. This is also confirmed by the fact that in Zvezda and other similar cows the fat content of the thermal portion of the residual milk, which is extracted after the normal residual milk has been obtained (Table 11), only differs from the latter by 0·6%, whereas it was 3·9% on average in the other cows.

The experimental data show that the individual greater or lesser ability of the animals to respond with an increase in synthesis in the mammary gland to more vigorous evacuation of the gland is dependent both on the reserves in the gland and on the capacity for "extended reproduction" of these reserves in response to their increased evacuation. The experimental data are an attempt to reveal individual peculiarities in cows in relation to the production of milk fat.

It would be interesting to extend these studies to the other constituents of milk.

The effect on milk secretion of the frequency with which the gland is emptied. Synthesis is stimulated to some extent if the discharge of the products of synthesis from the gland is somewhat forced. There is clearly a limit to this, and if this limit is surpassed the rate of synthesis may even be reduced. Here it is most important to stress that both in experiments involving the regular use of oxytocin and in our experiments with a thermal stimulus, the manipulation that led to the removal of milk was applied at the normal time of milking and the number of milkings was not increased. We were therefore concerned with more complete rather than more frequent evacuation of the udder.

Experts in animal husbandry are commonly and justifiably of the opinion that overfrequent milking, even of high-yielding cows, decreases rather than increases the yield. This is, of course, largely due to interruption of the very process of milk ejection, but this can hardly be the sole cause: it may be thought that in some cases we are dealing with a specific derangement in the processes of synthesis due to their being overstrained.

Some grounds for a hypothesis of this type have been obtained by Olenov from an experiment in which thermal stimuli were frequently applied to the udder. The experiment was carried out on two cows which had previously been found to react to thermal stimuli under normal farming conditions by a stable increase in the percentage of fat in the milk and an equally persistent increase in the daily output of milk fat. When thermal stimuli were applied frequently (every 30 min.) between milkings, one animal ceased to respond by the usual increase and there was even a considerable fall in milk yield and in the percentage of milk fat in the other animal, which led, naturally, to a sharp decline in the daily output of milk fat. This effect remained for $1\frac{1}{2}$ months after frequent thermal stimuli had been discontinued. In both cows frequent thermal stimuli caused an increase in the transfer of milk with a high fat content from the alveolar to the cisternal section, as was shown by the increased volume and higher fat content of the cisternal portion. One remarkable feature was that in the second cow this was observed a long time after the stimulus had been discontinued. The percentage of fat in the cisternal milk remained persistently at a higher level (4%) than in the alveolar milk (3·3%). This quite unusual fact shows in itself that there had been profound functional disturbance to the secretory and motor functions of the mammary gland. The results thus obtained were clearly due to serious overstraining of the function of the udder, caused by the forced removal of the products of synthesis from the alveolar cavities and possibly also from the cytoplasm of the secretory epithelium. Under the existing conditions forced discharge did not stimulate but depressed milk synthesis.

Tsakhaev (1959b) has studied the effect of overfrequent emptying of the udder on the composition of goat milk. Posterior-pituitary extract was injected and the residual milk obtained after the normal milking. The animal was then milked in different variants of the experiment at intervals of 15 min., 40 min. (with posterior-pituitary extract) or 60 min. (without posterior-pituitary extract). At intervals of 15 min., and to a lesser extent at 40 min., the percentage of fat first rose slightly and then fell to the same level as in the cisternal milk. There was a regular decline in casein content in each successive portion: total phosphorus content declined more significantly. When the period between milkings was increased, the composition of the milk in each successive portion was stabilized. These data show that forced evacuation of the udder has a negative effect. It is most probable that we are here concerned with considerable interruption in the synthetic activity of the gland under these conditions.

The findings of Azimov et al. (1961) are important for an explanation of Tsakhaev's results. They found from experiments involving the injection of radioactive phosphorus that forced evacuation of a goat's udder under conditions similar to those in the first variant of Tsakhaev's experiment (complete milking out followed by three injections of posterior-pituitary extract at intervals of 10 min. and remilking on each occasion) led to a sharp decline both in milk secretion and in reabsorption of labelled phosphate. Milking and the injection of posterior-pituitary extract did not intensify the transfer of phosphate from the storage system into the blood under these conditions, although it does so when the udder fills in the normal manner. The authors conclude that the presence of residual milk is essential if secretion is to be maintained. They suggest that the reabsorbed components of the residual milk stimulate the secretory activity of the mammary gland. These findings are of basic interest and undoubtedly provide the basis for full-scale studies.

The problem of the connexion between milk removal and

synthesis is certainly in need of further detailed analysis and it is difficult to overestimate its practical importance. Nevertheless, it still remains true, and is an axiom in animal husbandry, that any improvement in milking technique that gives good complete milking will only be fully effective if all the other conditions that make for a high milk yield (feeding, maintenance, etc.) are simultaneously improved.

It will be the purpose of the next and final chapter to assess the facts that have already been presented in the light of their importance in the day-to-day exploitation of a dairy cow, and especially in hand and machine milking. I have frequently cited practical experience to illustrate various theoretical points and have noted the importance of various physiological facts in the practice of dairy farming. Now I must show how some of the physiological features of the mammary gland can most rationally be exploited in practice in the normal course of work on a dairy farm.

CHAPTER FIVE

SOME FEATURES OF MAMMARY GLAND FUNCTION AND OF MILKING PRACTICE

The correct organization of milking should ensure that milking is as complete as possible and that the further synthesis of milk is stimulated as well as is possible. But this is not all. A no less important aspect is to ensure the greatest possible economy in labour and milking time and to reduce labour costs per unit of milk. It may seem that this is a purely economic problem that should not be considered in a physiological work. Such an approach would be incorrect in a case in which economy is closely related to physiology, and the assistance of physiology is sought in selecting and proving the correctness of a milking system and techniques that are both physiologically effective and cheap.

The milker's art is one of making the best use during milking of those physiological reactions of the animal that underlie the accumulation of milk and milk ejection. Milking should be carried out when the cow is most prepared for milk ejection. All the milker's actions in the period immediately before and during milking should be co-ordinated with the various stages of the motor reaction of the udder, so that this reaction is utilized and also stimulated in every possible way. If all these requirements are fulfilled, it is easier to milk the cow in the shortest possible time and as completely as possible without great exertion. All that has been said is, of course, equally applicable to hand and machine milking.

Milking frequency. This is of great practical importance. The major considerations are economic. There is extensive evidence, both from abroad and from some of our best farms, to show that milking twice a day has marked economic advantages, since it considerably reduces labour costs per unit of milk and allows work on the dairy farm to be planned in the most rational manner. These economic advantages are so apparent that no one contests them.

The opponents of twice-daily milking normally advance physiological rather than economic arguments in support of their opinion and we ought, therefore, to examine this aspect in detail.

Three main arguments are normally advanced by the opponents of twice-daily milking.

1. The udder capacity of most cows is not sufficient to hold all the milk that can be accumulated in a 12-hr. interval between milkings. The accumulation of excess milk in the storage system by the end of the period creates conditions that make secretion less effective.

2. Milking is in itself a stimulator of secretion by inducing reflex activity in the adenohypophysis and the discharge of the lactogenic hormone that is the main activator of the secretory function of the mammary gland.

3. In some cases the introduction of an additional milking leads to some increase in milk yields. It is therefore concluded that the introduction of additional milkings is an essential measure for further increase in yields at some stage in the development of the output of a herd.

Analysis of these arguments leads me to conclude that their significance is relative. Udder capacity is not an invariable quantity, but one which changes and varies in relation to the cow's yield and the training of the storage system of the udder. I have cited various proofs that the capacity of the udder is not governed merely by the total anatomical volume of the udder spaces, but is also related to the reflex physiological mechanism that varies the tone of the smooth musculature of the ducts and cisterns in conformity with the amount of milk that accumulates in the udder.

There are facts to show that in the majority of cows, including high-yielding cows (and possibly especially in high-yielding cows), the period of free milk synthesis, when secretion can occur without being impeded by a rise in pressure within the udder, is not only not less than 12 hr., but may sometimes be considerably longer. Beguchev (1950) has shown that, even in animals that have not had special preliminary training, milk secretion is not noticeably depressed until approximately 80% of the udder capacity is utilized, which takes about 12 hr. in most cows. To tell the truth, careful examination of Beguchev's facts leads to the conclusion that his opposition to twice-daily milking is not supported by his own findings. It is clearly not by accident that in the closing section of his paper Beguchev lays more stress on the harm that can be caused by milking too frequently than on the unsuitability of twice-daily milking. It would be interesting to repeat his experiments on cows accustomed to twice-daily milking.

Turner (1955a) had absolutely the same findings from an experiment on seven cows that had been milked twice a day before the experiment. It can be seen in Fig. 2 that the rate of milk synthesis was not lowered in any instance, even when the period between milkings was extended to 16 hr. or more. It is especially important to note that in Turner's experiments each animal was studied more than once at different stages in the lactation. It may be thought that the fact that secretion was so stable in this case was due to preliminary training of the cows, for whom long periods between milkings was not a new factor introduced in the course of the experiment.

In another paper Turner (1955c) makes a further analysis of the significance of irregular periods between milkings when milking twice a day in experiments on two groups of twin cows in their first lactation. One group was milked at 8- and 16-hr. intervals and the other at 11- and 13-hr. intervals. There was no great difference between the groups in the yield and fat content of the milk.

McMeekan and Brumby (1956) conducted the same experiment on twin cows for two lactations with 12-hr. intervals between milkings in one case and 16- and 8-hr. intervals in the other. They did not observe any significant variations in yield and in the total output of milk fat between the two groups. Elliot and Brumby (1955) came to precisely the same conclusions on the significance of irregular intervals when milking twice a day. There is also evidence that pressure within the udder cannot attain the critical level at which it interferes with secretion within 12 hr of milking.

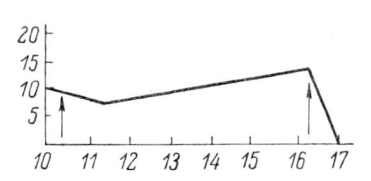

FIG. 37. Intracisternal pressure in the cow Beta when the interval between milkings was extended. (From Nikitin *et al.*, 1953.)

X-axis—time after previous milking (hr.); y-axis—pressure (mm. of mercury). Arrows: left—proper milking time (passed over); right—actual time of milking.

It has been shown in a paper by Nikitin *et al.* (1953) that when the normal milking time of cows milked at regular intervals four times a day is allowed to pass, the rise in pressure within the udder is extremely gradual. It can be seen in Fig. 37 that no further rise in pressure was observed in the cow Beta when the period between milkings was increased by omitting the second milking. The yield almost equalled that of the second and third milkings on ordinary days. Thus, in this case the secretion of milk was not reduced, despite such a serious alteration to the pattern to which the animal was accustomed as the omission of a regular milking.

It is probable that the capacity of the udder only becomes a factor that limits the secretion of milk under certain conditions, which must be taken into account. This will apply above all to cows that have just calved until the mammary gland becomes normal after calving and the capacity of the udder comes into line with the level of milk secretion, which is known to rise rapidly in the first weeks after calving. We recommend that such cows should be milked 3–4 times a day for not less than 2–3 weeks after calving. This is done on farms such as the "Road to a New Life" collective farm (Moscow region, Kuntsevo district) that have gone over to twice-daily milking.

Another exception to the rule is to be found in certain cows in which there is a marked discrepancy between udder capacity and output and whose yield declines noticeably and considerably if they are put on to twice-daily milking. Such cows are certainly to be found in every herd. This is an idiosyncrasy that it is difficult to overcome by training. Andreas (1954) suggests that this is an inherited attribute and that such cows should be the first to be rejected and should be gradually eliminated from the herd on farms where there is insistent economic pressure for transition to twice-daily milking. It will need further study to show whether or not udder capacity is inherited. It is, however, certainly true that in the breeding of dairy cattle one ought to consider such factors as udder capacity, even development of the separate quarters of the udder, the tightness of the teat sphincters and the rate of milk ejection in addition to yield and fat content. These are all important characteristics of the animal which have so far been largely ignored in breeding and which we have no right to ignore any longer in view of the general need for intensified dairy farming and complete mechanization of all labour processes on the dairy farm.

It is, at first sight, more difficult to refute the second objection to twice-daily milking, which is concerned with the stimulatory effect of milking on milk secretion. There are, in fact, no grounds for denying that milking affects both the function of the udder and the activity of all the systems of the organism that are in any way associated with the function of lactation. It would not, however, be quite correct to treat the secretion of milk between milkings as a reflex caused by milking. It is certain that the principle of multiple maintenance is involved in the maintenance of milk secretion. I have already mentioned Tverskoi's findings on the possibility of maintaining milk secretion even when the gland's connexions with the central nervous system have been totally destroyed, but this is, of course, an extreme case which only shows how flexible the organism can be. Under normal conditions, reflexes from the mammary gland during milking or suckling undoubtedly play a part in evacuating the udder and in maintaining secretion. In Tverskoi's opinion, those impulses from the udder that are associated with the filling and emptying of its storage system play a considerable part in maintaining secretion. The role of these impulses is certainly no less than that of the exteroceptive stimuli associated with stimulation of the skin of the teats during milking.

In assessing the significance of the frequency of milking to activation of the reflex apparatuses that control milk secretion, one must not forget another important circumstance—namely that the effectiveness of stimuli associated with milking can be quite different in relation to the animal's condition and its readiness for milking. We now have a great deal of information concerning milk ejection, from which we can conclude that its effectiveness in each cow under consideration is highly dependent on the fullness of the udder at the moment of milking. At a certain optimum level the length of the latent period of the reflex is considerably reduced and the rate of both hand and machine milking is increased. Existing data show that this optimum level is observed when 70–80% of the udder's physiological capacity is being utilized. According to Azimov and Beguchev, this corresponds to the close of the period of free milk synthesis. It is quite natural to assume that it is at this moment that all the influences that stimulate the activity of the mammary gland, including secretion, will be most effective.

It would be quite incorrect to ascribe the relative ease with which the udder is evacuated when very full to purely mechanical causes.

All our existing knowledge concerning milk ejection as an active process suggests that this ease is, in fact, due to the nature of the reflex reaction that develops in response to milking. I have already indicated that the excitability of the lactational centre only attains its maximum when a certain, fairly long period has elapsed after evacuation of the gland and that the signals reaching the centre from the filled storage system should be of fundamental significance in functional adjustment of the centre. It may be assumed that the optimum for exteroceptive secretory reflexes from the udder is also connected with a definite level of fullness in the storage system. Although experimental study of this question is still quite inadequate, this conclusion is certainly prompted by the well-known data on the negative effect of over-frequent milking even in very high-yielding cows.

The third objection to twice-daily milking—that there is a relatively slight increase in yield on transition to milking three or four times a day—should be considered more from an economic than from a physiological point of view.

There is extensive literature on the influence of the frequency of milking on yield, but the data in the different papers are often contradictory and are clearly highly dependent on the methods used in the experiments, the peculiarities of the cattle, feeding conditions and other factors. In a summary of experiments by foreign authors, Petersen (1950) quite justifiably points out that a great drawback to most of these experiments was their short duration. He cites Woodward's data from an experiment covering a complete lactation. In this experiment it was established that the lactation curve when the animal was milked three times a day was more stable than might be imagined from the results of brief experiments. Woodward's experimental data are reproduced in Fig. 38. A comparison of the yield curves throughout the lactation for milking twice and three times a day shows that there is some increase in yield when the animal is milked three times a day. One extremely interesting detail to be revealed is that in the first three months of the lactation the third milking had hardly any effect on output, and its full effect was only revealed by the beginning of the fifth month of the lactation. If this is so, the third milking is not necessary at the beginning of the lactation, as is now commonly accepted, but in the second half. One can also assume from Woodward's facts that in this case the effect of the additional (third) milking is more connected with an increase in reflex stimulation of the anterior hypophysis and increased discharge of the lactogenic hormone than with mechanical unloading of the udder. It is evident that the additional stimulation occasioned by the third milking is of importance in relation to the decline in the lactogenic activity of the adenohypophysis that has already been observed in the course of the lactation. I must, of course, stress that this aspect of Woodward's experiments is only of theoretical interest at present and must be further studied. It would be a great mistake to draw practical conclusions at this stage.

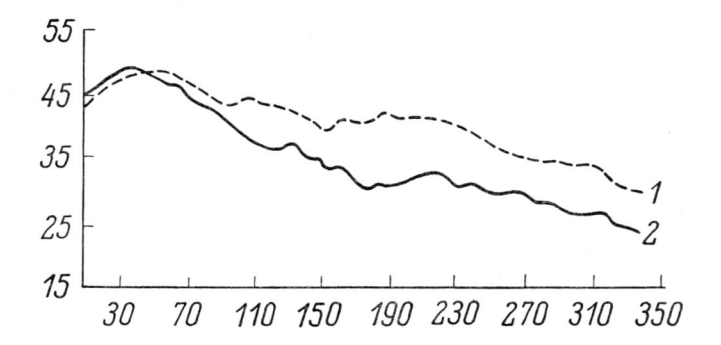

FIG. 38. The effect of three milkings (1) and two milkings (2) per day on the milk production of cows. (From Woodward *et al.*, 1936.)

X-axis—duration of lactation (days); *y-axis*—daily yield (lb.).

Petersen doubts whether one should change to milking three times a day, since his calculations (for the U.S.A.) show that this increases the cost of the milk by 50% and that this extra expenditure is not covered by the additional milk obtained.

It is quite clear that economic considerations are also largely involved under Soviet conditions. In considering the various possibilities of increasing milk output, we shall certainly give preference to those which are most effective in the given case and which make the least demands on the labour force. One can only decide whether it is more advantageous to spend time and money on an extra milking to obtain extra milk or whether the time should be spent on fodder production, by considering the actual conditions on each farm. The important factor here is that if the animals are well fed and cared for, twice-daily milking will not prevent milk output being raised to the highest possible level and maintained at that level. We can illustrate this by citing Andreas (1954), who milked a herd of 150 head twice a day for a year (Table 17).

TABLE 17

MAXIMUM DAILY AND SINGLE YIELD OF COWS OF DIFFERING YIELDS WHEN MILKED TWICE A DAY

Yield per cow per lactation (kg.)	Number of cows with this yield	Highest daily yield (kg.)	Highest single yield (kg.)
3000–4000	12	20·2	10·1
4000–5000	69	24·6	12·3
5000–6000	57	27·6	13·8
6000 and over	12	30·2	15·1

Twice-daily milking did not prevent him from obtaining extremely high yields from the herd. Of the 150 cows, 69 gave more than 5000 kg. of milk during the lactation, and the udders of the highest-yielding cows were able to accommodate more than 15 kg. without difficulty.

The basic conclusion to be drawn from this is that milking twice a day does not limit the output of milk that can be attained by correct handling of the animals.

Preparation of the cow for milking. The basic significance of the circumstances preceding milking is that, if routine on the farm is adhered to fairly strictly, the animals become accustomed to a definite pattern. When this pattern is reproduced it stimulates commencement of reactions in the mammary gland connected with the first stage of milk ejection. If the lactation centre of the animal is highly excitable it may sometimes activate the second stage before milking of the teats commences.

The time at which milking begins and the order in which the cows in the group are milked becomes of great importance as a signal: sudden change in these two conditions may lead to partial or even total inhibition of milk ejection in some cows. There are also cows that are fairly indifferent to such changes. A great deal of work will still be necessary before we can establish which elements in a situation are of particular importance. In the meantime one must attempt not to alter unnecessarily the pattern to which the animal is accustomed. Nevertheless, it is certainly wrong to exaggerate the importance of the pattern which the animal has "learnt by heart" and to make it an insurmountable obstacle to the introduction of any changes in conditions in the cowshed, even when such changes would certainly effect considerable improvements. One often hears that this conservatism is based on "the profoundly scientific principles of Pavlov's theory of higher nervous activity". This is, of course, quite untrue. The true biological significance of the mechanisms of temporary connexions is that they allow flexible adaptation of the animal to the changing conditions of the external environment, and existing temporary connexions are extinguished or inhibited as new ones are formed. This means that the cow can easily be accustomed to quite different milking conditions. Thus, for example, foreign experience of the organization of special milking sheds (which is now being applied and developed on some of our best farms) shows that cows can not only be accustomed to give milk under the new conditions but can also be accustomed to come to the milking shed for milking when a signal is given. It is, for example, noteworthy that an Australian farmer (Mr. Maff) thought it economically worth while to get rid of those cows that for various reasons found it difficult to accustom themselves to the new conditions when he set up a special milking shed on his farm.

Nothing but harm can be caused to the rational planning of our dairy farms by vulgarizations of the fundamentals of Pavlov's theory of higher nervous activity. The conditions to which the cows are accustomed can and should always be changed when this is required for organizational reasons. The important point is not to impose tasks on the animal that are beyond the scope of its higher nervous activity or that it finds difficult to perform. This applies, in particular, to the interval from the commencement of preparing for milking until milking actually begins in both hand and machine milking, but especially in the latter. This time should be reduced as much as possible. The milkmaid's arrival, her voice, the clatter of the milk pail, raising the animal, cleaning the coat, washing the udder and preliminary massage are all conditioned and unconditioned stimuli of the reflexes of the first, and sometimes of the second stage of milk ejection. Even before milking commences, the correct employment of these stimuli relaxes the teat sphincters and the musculature of the cisterns and ducts and often starts the discharge of milk from the ducts into the cistern: in brief, it creates the most favourable background for the reflex of the second stage, for contraction of the alveoli and expulsion of the major part of the milk into the cisterns. Any delay in commencing milking after preparation is complete worsens the result, extends the total duration of milking and affects the yield and especially the fat content. The practice of preparing for milking 5 minutes or more beforehand, which is sometimes encountered, is a serious infringement of normal milking procedure. Apart from not allowing any time to elapse between preparation for milking and its commencement, one should also ensure that the successive manipulations involved in preparation are carried out as quickly as possible. Massage and washing and drying the udder should be rapid as well as brisk and thorough.

The effect of massage and of washing the udder before milking is, in general, manifested in the same way. Their direct effect on milk ejection is to be found in reflex relaxation of the tone of the cistern and the mouths of the ducts facilitating expulsion of milk from the alveoli into the cisterns in the second stage and, if the udder is sufficiently full, causing milk to enter the cisterns before the commencement of the second stage.

The effect of washing the udder is greatly enhanced if the temperature of the water is 53–56°C. This method of preparing the udder for milking greatly speeds up the onset of the second stage of milk ejection, and is especially advantageous in machine milking. Apart from my own studies, there is now a great deal of confirmation in our literature on animal husbandry that this procedure should be generally introduced. I shall not enumerate all the publications dealing with this question, but shall content myself with reference to the papers of Lyapustin and Bulak (1952) and Tyarkin (1953), whose experiments have shown that washing the udder with hot water has a positive effect on milk ejection and on the total output of milk fat. The only communication known to me that failed to confirm my findings is that by Tsibizov and Lebedev (1955). It is true that, in their experiment on five cows of the Yaroslav breed, Tsibizov and Lebedev did not wash the udder with hot water, but subjected it to considerably longer heating (which explains the somewhat bizarre title of their paper: "The effect of warm heating of the udder...", and this makes it difficult to compare their negative results with the positive results obtained by other authors, including myself.

Many foreign authors also recommend that the udder should be washed with hot water to facilitate milking (Smith and Petersen, 1948; Jensen, 1949; Christensen, 1949; Bílek and Doležalek, 1954; and others). In his rules of milking, Petersen (1950) states quite bluntly that: "The most effective stimulus (of milk ejection— M.Z.) is vigorous massage of the teats and the lower part of the udder by a cloth taken out of water as hot as the hands will stand— about 125°F. This stimulates both the warmth and touch receptors in the skin of the teat." Whittlestone (1951) points out that heat (water up to 60°C.) can re-establish the milk-ejection reflex if it has been inhibited by an experimental pain stimulus or in cases of mastitis, and can also "correct" the milking curves of cows that respond poorly to machine milking.*

The hygienic importance of washing the udder with hot water should also be taken into consideration. Kasalainen found in our laboratory that the regular washing with hot water reduced to a quarter the amount of bacteria in 1 ml. of fresh milk (24,000 to 6000). Bílek and Doležalek have also noted a considerable improvement in the hygienic properties of the milk.

All these advantages are so apparent that one could recommend that the udder should be washed with hot water even if it did not have a positive effect on fat content. There is, therefore, no reason to discontinue the practice on cows that do not respond by increased output of milk fat, since the thermal stimuli still affect the rate of milking and hygienic properties.

Udder massage. A great many studies in animal husbandry have been devoted to udder massage in lactating cows, in relation to technique and effectiveness. The results have mainly been assessed from production tests in which milk output and the percentage and total output of fat are taken into consideration. These findings show that the use of preliminary and concluding massage in milking is fully justified. Our information on the actual physiological mechan-

*Washing the udder with hot water was commenced independently and almost simultaneously in the U.S.S.R. and in various foreign countries. Two workers on the Suoryavi State Farm in Kazakhstan (the milkmaid K. M. Letsko and the animal husbandry specialist A. I. Mashkova) were, however, the first to note its special effect on fat content and should be given the credit.

isms that underlie the beneficial effect of massage during milking is considerably less complete. I have already mentioned the available information more than once and now only need to summarize the main conclusions, some of which remain provisional.

1. Massage has basically a reflex effect that is only partly due to simple mechanical expulsion of milk into the cisterns from the large-calibre ducts.

2. The basic effect of massage is its influence on the tone of the smooth musculature of the ducts and cisterns of the mammary gland. This effect is arrived at by a purely reflex pathway, without the participation of a humoral link. Sufficiently intensive and more prolonged massage can invoke a neurohumoral reflex and the discharge of oxytocin, especially in animals that react most easily, but this is the exception rather than the rule.

3. Deep massage, especially at the end of milking, can be instrumental in freeing part of the residual milk from the alveoli, by direct activation of the myoepithelial cells.

4. Massage improves blood circulation and lymph flow in the udder. This effect is connected with the fact that massage assists the purely mechanical flow of venous blood and lymph as well as with vasomotor reflexes. This aspect of the effect of massage is of particular importance in oedema and induration of the udder in newly-calved cows.

Massage is important to the growth and development of the gland as well as in freeing it of milk. In non-lactating animals, such as calves, virgin goats and heifers, udder massage can cause growth and development of the mamary gland. This makes lactation possible in non-pregnant animals; massage of pregnant heifers increases milk yield by comparison with animals that have not been massaged if the massage is commenced before calving. The effect of massage on the development of the gland is, however, somewhat outside the scope of this book.

There are various descriptions of the ways in which the udder can be massaged during milking (Davidov, 1950; Al'tman, 1951; Bogdashev and Eliseev 1951, etc.). All the authors stress that the procedure should not be unduly standardized and recommend that both the duration and the method should be varied in relation to the anatomical features of the udder and the reactivity of the animal: this recommendation is certainly quite correct. The quite detailed gives rise to a stronger unconditioned milk-ejection reflex.

The rate of milking should be such as to ensure that the udder is emptied as completely as possible in the period of active milk ejection, and also that the physiological optimum for the muscles of the milker's wrist is not overstepped. I have already cited data concerning the optimum frequency of stimuli for the milk-ejection reflex and noted that the optimum rate is not fixed and established once and for all for any animal or even for the same animal, but depends on the stage of the lactation and on the animal being accustomed to a given rate of milking. It is usually recommended that the teats should be squeezed 90–110 times a minute; it is clear that there is an average optimum that can vary in relation to the given conditions.

Little attention has as yet been paid to milking rhythm. Special studies are still necessary to decide whether it is better to carry out the whole milking at a constant rate or whether the rate should be increased and decreased in conformity with the cow's reaction to milking. Although, as I have mentioned, this question has still not been studied in sufficient detail, experienced milkers do not maintain an invariable rate, but vary both the rate and the strength of squeezing in relation to the way in which the cow "lets down" her milk. This is clearly not without physiological significance. Leontovich and his colleagues (1932) pay quite justifiable attention to this and are certainly correct to point out that calves do not suckle at an unchanging rate, but that the strength of suckling (by the calf— M.Z.) is adapted to the activity of the gland in milk removal. Milkers also apparently do this to some extent. These considerations are of particular importance in machine milking.

Fundamental importance is also atttached to the sequence in which the quarters of the udder are milked. Of the three main methods now used (milking one side, criss-cross and "direct" milking), the "direct" method, in which first the fore and then the rear quarters, or vice versa, are milked, is usually considered to be the best. The majority of our best milkers use this method. Its advantages have also been established in prolonged tests by Troshin (1936). It is also recommended by Jensen (1949) in his paper on teaching the correct technique of hand milking. According to Troshin, direct milking increases both the yield and the percentage of fat in the milk (Table 18).

TABLE 18
EFFECT OF MILKING METHOD ON YIELD AND FAT CONTENT
(FROM I. P. TROSHIN)

Method	Fat %	Amount of milk given (kg.)
Direct milking	3·80	100·0
One-sided milking	3·68	95·8
Criss-cross	3·59	94·0

In studying these results in the past, I (Zaks, 1955) have tried to explain them exclusively on the basis that the "direct" method ensures the most even evacuation of the udder, which is of particular importance, since milk ejection occurs simultaneously throughout the udder during milking. I have considered that in "direct" milking the milker is able to empty the fore quarters and transfers her attention to the rear quarters before milk ejection has become less energetic in them. I still think that these considerations are valid. It should be remembered, however, that this is not the only advantage of the "direct" method: it is also better adapted to the milker's own exertions. In the "direct" method both hands play an equal part in milking the fore and rear quarters, whereas in the criss-cross method, for example, the less-developed quarters are always milked with the right hand and the rear quarters, which are more developed, are milked with the left. This can mean that they are less carefully milked. The importance of this feature should not be underestimated.

All-round mechanization of all farming processes, which is a pressing problem in dairy farming, cannot be achieved without changing over everywhere from hand to machine milking. Further study of the physiological effects of machine milking and the elaboration of new and improved methods for its use is therefore an urgent necessity.

Development of the technique of machine milking has quite a long history. The first proposals, which date back to 1819 in the U.S.A., were based on the insertion of catheters into the teat cavities and subsequent drainage of the milk. This method was soon found to be quite unsuitable owing to the damage that it caused and to frequent infection of the teats. A multitude of proposals based on methods that reproduced the manipulations of hand milking in various ways were also found to be equally impracticable. They all required relatively large amounts of mechanical force and the animals found them difficult to tolerate. The first milking machines based on the principle of sucking out the milk were designed in 1860, but they were unsatisfactory because they employed a high steady vacuum which did great damage to the teat. It was only late in the nineteenth century that the correct principle of a variable vacuum, on which all subsequent designs have been based, was suggested. The introduction of the pulsator, which converts a constant vacuum into a pulsating vacuum in the teat-cups, was a particularly important step. All modern milking machines are based on various modifications of this principle.

The Soviet "three-phase" milking machine has one important advantage. The alternation of vacuum, compression and rest minimizes the harmful effects of leaving the teat-cups on the teats for a long period.

I shall not dwell on the most important advantages of machine milking, since they are quite well known. It is much more important to give an account of certain drawbacks, which are not dealt with as fully as could be desired in the existing manuals on machine milking. This aspect is, moreover, of basic importance for further improvements in the design of milking machines. I am thinking, in the main, of the physiological effects of machine milking rather than of the economic features and performance of these machines.

It is quite widely held that the action of a teat-cup should imitate the suckling motions of the calf's mouth,* This tendency on the part of designers might be accepted, but for the fact that the ideal is not attained in any of the existing types of milking device. The main

---

*Although I am in general agreement with the opinion of Leontovich and others that the mechanism of suckling should be taken into consideration when designing milking apparatus, I do not think that it would be entirely correct to copy this act slavishly. The suckling reflex of the calf, like that of the young of other mammals, has been formed in the process of evolution in relation to its biological features and requirements. The amount of milk formed and the duration of lactation in the modern dairy cow are much greater than the milk requirements of the calf. Suckling by the calf is not intended to empty the udder entirely (in a high-yielding cow), whereas completeness of milking is an essential condition in hand and machine milking.

differences between the act of suckling and the working of a teat-cup are as follows.

1. From the time that it is put on the teat to the time that it is removed the teat-cup functions at an even rate and strength. The rate and strength of the calf's suckling motions vary as the act of milk ejection develops (Leontovich et al., 1932).

2. The milking machine continues to work after milking has ceased. The calf stops suckling, of its own volition or under compulsion, as soon as the quarter of the udder is completely or almost completely emptied.

3. The action of the teat-cup is mainly restricted to the central and lower thirds of the teat; the most important reflexogenic zone at the base of the teat is not stimulated, and this may be the reason for the relative weakness of the milk-ejection reflex in certain cows that can only be stimulated with difficulty in machine milking. The calf has a strong stimulatory effect on all zones of the teat.

4. The calf combines suckling with energetic massage of the udder in a most highly developed form. Massage is totally absent in the working of a teat-cup.

5. The teats of a cow do not hang perpendicular to the ground, but somewhat obliquely from back to front. The veins and lymph vessels are similarly orientated. Whereas the suckling motions of the calf's mouth follow the longitudinal axis of the teat quite closely, the "exertions" of a teat-cup are applied along an axis perpendicular to the ground. This does not entirely conform to the anatomical structure of the teat, and Azimov, for one, thinks that this is of basic significance.

These, in my opinion, are the most important anatomical and physiological considerations which should be allowed for in further improvements in the design of milking machines.

The main complaint usually voiced against the use of milking machines is that one has to follow machine milking by hand stripping. In the greater majority of cows some milk (which is also the part of the yield richest in fat) has to be milked out after the teat-cups have been removed.

I regret that we still have no precise explanation for this fact. Those who suggest that part of the explanation is bad use of the milking machine are certainly correct. Failure to prepare the cow properly for milking, putting on the teat-cups too soon or too late, overmilking by regularly leaving the teat-cups in position after milking out has ended, frequent and unnecessary changes in the precise routine of milking and similar mistakes will certainly make machine milking less effective and increase the amount of hand stripping.

The main recommendations for reducing the relative volume of milk obtained by hand stripping or eliminating hand stripping altogether are also certainly correct. These recommendations are as follows.

1. Not to commence machine milking when the udder is not very full. This is even more important in machine than in hand milking.

2. Not to apply the teat-cups before the reflexes of the first stage of milk ejection cause milk to move into the teat cisterns. This can be seen from expansion of the teats and the smoothing out of the wrinkles on their skin.

3. To massage each quarter of the udder separately as soon as the flow of milk declines (which can be seen through the sight glass).

4. While massaging the quarters of the udder (especially their lower portions) when the flow of milk declines, draw the teat-cups slightly downwards. Petersen attaches great importance to this technique, since he considers that there is a purely mechanical obstruction to the movement of milk from the cistern of the gland into the teat cavity at a certain stage in the emptying of the udder, which is eliminated by drawing down the teat-cups. According to Belyaevskii (1960) however, the reasons for this are physiological as well as mechanical. Partial evacuation of the cistern and ducts leads to a rise in their tone (see p. 70 and Figs. 26 and 28), which increases the significance of the mechanical obstruction. Belyaevskii recommends that as soon as milking out has ceased the teat-cup assembly should be thrust downward and forward, using a fair amount of force, and that massage of the udder should be carried out with the other hand. This technique ("machine stripping") makes hand stripping unnecessary in most cows.

These techniques certainly have some importance, but they do not always suffice to remove all the milk from every cow. Further research will be necessary before we can dispense with hand stripping. We must first establish where the milk which is subsequently removed by hand stripping is located in the storage system when the teat-cups are removed. Strange as it may seem, we still do not know the answer to this apparently simple question. In Petersen's opinion all the milk that has actually entered the cisterns can be entirely removed by the machine. Thus, according to Petersen, incomplete milking is always due to incomplete milk ejection and retention of part of the milk in the ducts and alveoli. (An exception to this is milk that may be retained in the cistern of the gland and fail to enter the teat cavity for purely mechanical reasons.)

This explanation is scarcely applicable to every case. I have found in a number of cases that after complete milking out by machine, some milk which remained in the cistern till the end of milking, and which the machine was unable to remove, can be obtained without preliminary manipulations if a catheter is inserted into the teat canal immediately after removal of the teat-cups. The amount of this milk varied between 10 and 100–125 ml. from each quarter of the udder in separate cows and also in the same cow at different milkings. The simplest assumption is that retention of this type is connected with resistance of the teat sphincters; the flow of milk ceases as soon as the vacuum can no longer overcome the tone of the sphincters. Since the vacuum remains almost unchanged throughout milking, we are clearly concerned with an increase in the tone of the sphincters at the end of milking. This aspect has been little studied. According to Leontovich, the resistance of the sphincters is subject to considerable variation in machine milking. The vacuum needed to overcome the resistance of the teat sphincters varies between 2 and 30 mm. of mercury in different cows and may be even greater on rare occasions. Leontovich also notes that resistance is relatively higher at the beginning of milking and that it declines gradually.

Uneven development of the separate quarters of the udder, which causes milking to be completed at different times and prolongs total milking time, is often mentioned as one of the complications in machine milking. The harmful effect of milking "empty" the less-developed quarters is also noted. American designers have suggested machines in which each cup is switched off automatically when milk ceases to flow, but these designs have not been taken up, mainly because of their high cost.

Martyugin (1954) considers, in general, that too much importance is attached to this factor. He found that the high-yielding quarters of the udder were milked at a somewhat faster rate than those that gave less milk and that therefore the duration of overmilking due to uneven development of the separate quarters of the udder did not, on average, exceed 9% of the total time spent in machine milking.

Martyugin's results in no way clash with Azimov's well-known hypothesis that the extent to which the udder is filled is of importance to the rate of milking; it is possible that this hypothesis is applicable to each separate quarter as well as to the udder as a whole. The question must be further studied.

SUPPLEMENT

ELASTOMETRIC STUDIES OF THE MOTOR FUNCTION OF THE MAMMARY GLAND IN WOMAN

The present state of our knowledge of the physiology of the mammary gland in the woman lags far behind the great progress that has been made in the lactational physiology of animals. This is largely because the methods used for experimental study of lactation in animals can rarely be applied to women. Development of the lactational physiology of the woman now depends, in the main, on the elaboration of new research methods that are both adequate and without harmful effects.

The "elastometric" method for studying the mammary gland of the woman that has been devised in Professor Ginetsinskii's laboratory (Ginetsinskii et al., 1958) is therefore of interest. The method is based on a principle put forward by Gildemeister (Gildemeister 1914; Springer, 1914) for determining the tone of the skeletal muscles by ballistic measurement of their elasticity. In applying this method to the mammary gland, we proceeded on the assumption that its elastic stress varies in relation to the fullness of the storage system and the tone of its contractile elements, i.e., on the same factors that also govern changes in pressure within the storage system.

Essentially the method is as follows. A metal disc (approx. 20 mm. in diameter) with a conical metal elevation in the centre is made to adhere to the skin near the areola of the nipple. A little hammer, suspended like a pendulum on a horizontal axis, falls from a known low height on to the disc and rebounds from the cone. If all the conditions associated with the pendulum remain constant, the time for which the hammer is in contact with the cone is exclusively determined by the elastic properties of the gland. The contact time is measured by reading from the scale of a ballistic galvanometer incorporated in a circuit which is switched on when the hammer falls and switched off when it rebounds. The contact time decreases as the elasticity increases and vice versa. Changes in the elasticity of the gland can be detected and their magnitude estimated from the alteration in the contact time in two successive readings. The contact time $t = KN$, where N is the deviation of the galvanometer scale in mm. and K is a constant which can be calculated easily if the electric parameters of the circuit are known. It may be possible to ignore this constant in practice. If the circuit voltage is constant the results can be expressed in conventional units (deviation of the galvanometer in mm.).

Changes that occur in the elastic stress of the gland as a result of its filling and emptying, or of an increase in the tone of its contractile elements due to the action of exogenous or endogenous oxytocin, or of the reaction of the myoepithelium to mechanical stimuli, etc., are reflected with sufficient accuracy by this method.

A number of facts concerning the capacity function of the mammary gland in the woman have been established by the use of this method (Soo, 1959). In the first days of lactation the rise in tension in the gland between feeds is directly proportional to the time that has elapsed since feeding. Later on in the lactation, however, this relation becomes quite different: the proportionality between the rise in tension and the time that has elapsed since feeding is only observed in the first 3-4 hr. after feeding. There is hardly any increase in tension between 4 and 7 hr., but the increase recommences in the 8th hour. Thus the rise in tension in the mammary gland of the woman at later stages in the lactation is reminiscent of the dynamics of pressure changes within the udder between milkings which I have established in cows in which the capacity function of the udder has been well trained. It is apparent that there is active regulation of the tone of the contractile elements of the storage system of the mammary gland in the woman as it fills. Milk therefore accumulates without a significant rise in pressure. In the initial period of the lactation this mechanism has not yet had time to become established.

It has also been established by elastometry that immediately after feeding commences in the first days of lactation there is a more or less significant rise in pressure in the other breast, apparently connected with the reflex discharge of oxytocin. In some women this rise in tension is rapidly followed by a decline, and tension in the other breast returns to the initial level after feeding. In other cases pressure remains high throughout feeding and returns slowly to the initial level at the end of feeding. In many cases in the later stages of lactation, however, the rise in tension in the other breast is less marked, and although pressure rises at the commencement of the feed, it falls rapidly and remains low during the feed. It is apparent that the return of pressure to the initial level in the breast that is not being emptied is connected with a relaxation reflex similar to that which I have described in cows. This reaction is even more clearly expressed in the mammary gland of the woman. The pressure drop within the gland as a result of this reaction is probably of particular importance in women, in whom the storage system is less developed than in cows and goats. Immediately after feeding there is a sharp decline in the elastic stress of the evacuated gland. In pathological induration of the mammary glands, which often occurs in women on the 3rd or 4th day of lactation, the decline in tension in the gland after it has been emptied is considerably less than under normal conditions. In opposition to the accepted opinion, we have assumed that induration is more connected with the retention of milk, inadequate and difficult evacuation of the gland due to a weakness in the milk-ejection reflex, than with hyperaemia and forced secretion.

Mazhbits (1961) has studied the quantitative relationship between the amount of milk suckled by the child and that drawn off after feeding in normal lactation and in induration of the breast. He has established that under normal conditions the average amount of milk suckled by the child (the distinction is statistically significant) is twice the amount that remains in the breast and is drawn off after feeding. It stands to reason that this is true when the child's food requirement is not lowered. In induration of the breast this ratio is reversed and the child suckles less milk than can be drawn off after feeding. It has been established that there are two clinical forms of induration: one is primarily connected with the retention of milk, normally in separate, unevenly distributed lobules, while the other is connected with more regular swelling of the parenchyma of the gland; the evacuation of milk is affected in both cases, but especially in the first. Subcutaneous injection of posterior-pituitary extract and other drugs containing oxytocin (0·5–1·5 i.u.) rapidly cures induration and restores lactation to normal. It is not necessary to use other therapeutic techniques (application of cold, laxatives, restricted intake of liquid, etc.).

We have found from elastometric measurement of the mammary gland that oxytocin begins to be effective within 1–2 min. of its subcutaneous injection. Tension in the gland rises rapidly and is maintained for 10–15 min., after which it begins to decline. In cases of induration, therefore, oxytocin should be injected after feeding, when the child has already been given the breast. If oxytocin is administered with a different object, such as causing contraction of the womb, we recommend that it should also be injected at the time of feeding. Our findings on the beneficial effect of oxytocin in cases of induration of the breast do not conflict in the main with those of the authors whose works have been summarized by Harris (1958).

The elastometric method enables one to detect changes in the turgor of the breast connected with development of its parenchyma in pregnancy and in the course of the menstrual cycle (Soo, 1959), as well as those connected with the tone of its contractile elements. The elasticity increases at the beginning of pregnancy, but falls somewhat at the end of the first half of pregnancy; it begins to rise again in the second half and reaches its highest point a few weeks before confinement. Tension in the mammary gland once again falls slightly immediately before confinement in the majority of women studied. The dynamics of changes in the elasticity of the mammary gland during pregnancy tally closely with changes in hormone activity established by Geschikter (1947) from a study of the excretion of oestrogens and pregnanediol in the urine.

The elasticity of the mammary glands is at its lowest immediately after menstruation commences. It then rises and reaches its highest point on the 14th or 15th day of the cycle, before again declining at the beginning of the next menstruation. These changes are most marked in childless women.

REFERENCES

Russian References with Translated Titles

AIZENBUDAS, L. B. 1957a. New instruments for studying the dynamics of milk and fat removal in the process of milking. *Byull. nauchno-tekhn informatsii* (Lithuanian Animal Husbandry and Veterinary Research Institute), No. 1, 39–43.

——1957b. Changes in fat content in successive portions of a milking. Ibid., No. 2, 27–31. (See also 1958, No. 3, 3–39, for another article by the same author and Lazauskas and Pakarskite.)

——1957c. Diurnal variations in the milk output of cows. *Vestnik s-kh. nauki,* No. 10, 106–13.

——1958. Reactivity of the constitution in farm animals. *Zh. obshch. biologii,* **19,** No. 1, 3–31.

ALIEV, M. T. 1956. On the physiology of milk ejection in water buffaloes. Second Transcaucasian Congress of Physiologists, Biochemists and Pharmacologists, Summary of Proceedings. Tbilisi, pp. 16–17.

AL'TMAN, A. D. 1945. Changes in the udder of cows during the process of milking. *Vestn. zhivotnovodstva,* No. 1, 85–96.

——1951. *Correct milking.* Sel'khozgiz, Moscow.

ARZUMANYAN, E. A. 1952. Changes in the mammary gland of Tagil calves and cows connected with lactation and age. *Sov. zootekhniya,* No. 1, 78–88.

ASRATYAN, E. A. 1935. The effect of posterior-pituitary extract on conditioned alimentary salivation reflexes. *Arkh. biolog. nauk,* **37,** No. 1, 87.

ASTRAKHANSKAYA, N. A. 1955. The importance of the nervous system to the development and functioning of the mammary gland. Author's summary of thesis. Leningrad.

AZIMOV, G. I. 1955. Aspects of milk fat yield. *Zhurn. obshch. biolog.,* **16,** No. 4, 249–62.

——1956. Pressing problems in lactational physiology. *Zhivotnovodstvo,* No. 12, 12–20.

AZIMOV, G. I., KRINITSIN, D. YA., & POPOV, N. F. 1954. *The physiology of farm animals.* Sel'khozgiz, Moscow, p. 31.

AZIMOV, G. I., & LAPINER, M. N. 1939. The number of milkings. *Sots. zhivotnovodstvo,* No. 5, 31-6.

——1940. Aspects of the physiology of a high-yielding cow. *Sov. zootekhniya,* No. 7, 47–60.

AZIMOV, G. I., ORLOV, A. F., & BELUGINA, O. P. 1961. Milk secretion and the laws that govern it. *Zhivotnovodstvo,* No. 1, 40–48.

BARYSHNIKOV, I. A. 1960. New data on the neurohumoral regulation of lactation. Papers presented to a scientific gathering of institutes of higher education to commemorate the fortieth anniversary of the Tatar ASSR, 247–49. Kazan.

BARYSHNIKOV, I. A., BORSUK, V. N., ZAKS, M. G., ZOTIKOVA, E. S., PAVLOV, G. N., & TOLBUKHIN, V. I. 1953. On nervous regulation of the activity of the mammary gland. *Zhurn. obshch, biologii,* **14,** No. 4, 257–74.

BARYSHNIKOV, I. A., ZAKS, M. G., ZOTIKOVA, I. N., LEVITSKAYA, E. S., PAVLOV, G. N., PAVLOV, E. F., TVERSKOI, G. B., TOLBUKHIN, V. I., & TSAKHAEV, G. A. 1951. Nervous regulation of the motor function of the mammary gland. *Zhurn. obshch. biologii,* **12,** No. 6, 423–39.

BEGUCHEV, A. P. 1950. The frequency of milking for cows. *Sov. zootekhniya,* No. 2, 31–43.

BELYAEVSKII, YU. A. 1960. Machine milking without hand stripping. *Zhivotnovodstvo,* No. 9, 74–6.

REFERENCES

BOGDASHEV, N. F., & ELISEEV, A. P. 1951. *The cow's udder.* Sel'khozgiz. Moscow, Leningrad.
——1957. *The mammary glands of farm animals.* 2nd edit., Sel'khozgiz, Moscow, Leningrad.
BORSUK, V. N. 1955a. On water-salt exchange in cows. *Tr. Inst. fiziol. im. I. P. Pavlova AN SSSR*, **4**, 198-209.
——1955b. Conditioned reflex regulation of milk removal from the ducts of the udder in cows. Second conference on the physiology of farm animals, Summary of Proceedings. Moscow, Leningrad.
——1957a. Conditioned reflex regulation of milk removal from the ducts of the udder in cows. *Problems of the physiology of farm animals*, 281-92. Akad. Nauk SSSR.
——1957b. Conditioned reflex regulation of the removal of milk from the alveoli of the mammary gland in cows. *Op. cit.*, 293-302.
BORSUK, V. N., & ZAKS, M. G. 1955. Distribution of fat and casein in successive portions of a single milking in cows. *Tr. Inst. fiziol. im. I. P. Pavlova AN SSSR*, **4**, 81-92.
DANILOV, A. A. 1940. *New data on the physiology of the hypophysis.* Akad. Nauk SSSR, Moscow, Leningrad.
DAVIDOV, R. B. 1950. *Milk and butter production.* Sel'khozgiz, Moscow.
DAVYDOV, S. G., FEDOTOVA, E. P., & KRASNOKUTSKAYA, A. I. 1939. The importance of the intensity of milk accumulation, the reaction of the cow to the milking process and the size of the udder to the yield of dairy cattle. *Tr. Pushkinsk. s.-kh. inst.*, **9**, 7-42.
DELOV, V. E., & PETROVA, E. G. 1948. The interaction of conditioned and unconditioned influences on the cardiac muscle (from electrophysiological indices). 13th Conference on physiological problems, Summary of Proceedings, 35-7.
DYUSEMBIN, KH. 1957a. The mechanism by which milk removal is inhibited. *Problems of the physiology of farm animals*, 310-15. Akad. Nauk SSSR, Moscow, Leningrad.
——1957b. The mechanism of the reflex inhibition of milk ejection. Op. cit., 316-24.
EGOROVA, A. A., ZAKS, M. G., OLENOV, YU. M., KASALAINEN, A. F., & SALTUP, B. N. 1953. Data from animal husbandry and physiology concerning the method of washing the udder with hot water. *Sov. zootekhniya*, No. 5, 46.
FEDII, E. M. 1961. Change in the synthesis and secretion of milk fat in cows under the influence of external environmental factors via the interoceptors. *Zhurn. obshch. biologii*, **22**, No. 1, 75-7.
GARKAVI, O. V. 1936. Milking twice and three times a day. *Usp. zootekhn. nauk*, **2**, No. 1, 133-47.
GINETSINSKII, A. G., VASIL'YEVA, V. F., ZAKS, M. G., SOKOLOVA, M. M., & SOO, V. A. 1958. A method for studying the capacity function of the mammary gland in the woman. *Akusherstvo i ginekologiya*, No. 5, 104-6.
GLEBINA, E. I. 1940. Development of the mammary gland and its secretory process. *Arkh. anat. gistol. i embriologii*, **22**, 332.
GOFMAN, M. A. 1953. New data on the reflex regulation of milk ejection. Author's summary of thesis. Leningrad.
——1955. Reflex regulation of milk ejection. *Tr. Inst. fiziol. im. I. P. Pavlova AN SSSR*, **4**, 22-33.
GORODETSKAYA, I. I. 1953. The effect of posterior-pituitary extract on the conditioned reflex activity of birds. *Uch. zap. Tomsk. gos. ped. inst.*, **10**, 392-405.
GRACHEV, I. I. 1949. Reflexes from the mammary gland. *Zhurn. obshch. biologii*, **10**, 401-20.

REFERENCES

———1951a. Fistula of the mammary gland. *Byull. eksperim. biol. i med.*, **31**, 45–6.
———1951b. A conditioned reflex to the activity of the mammary gland. *Dokl. Akad. Nauk SSSR*, **78**, 383–6.
———1952a. Reflex interactions between the mammary gland and the digestive system. *Dokl. Akad. Nauk, SSSR*, **84**, 397–400.
———1952b. The formation of a conditioned milk removal reflex on the basis of mechanical stimulation of the teat. *Dokl. Akad. Nauk SSSR*, **86**, 441–4.
———1953. The cerebral cortex and lactation. *Zhurn. obshch. biologii*, **14**, 333–48.
GUREVICH, B. KH., & KOLESNIKOV, M. S. 1955. Determination of the type of nervous system in animals left free to move about. *Fiziol. zh. SSSR*, **41**, 339–45.
INIKHOV, G. S. 1951. *The chemistry of milk and milk products.* Sel'khozgiz, Moscow.
KOBOZEV, V. S. 1953. The use of a four-chamber, three-phase milking machine in the machine milking of cows without hand stripping. *Tr. Vsesoyuzn. n.-i. inst. gibridiz. i akklimatiz. zhivotnykh "Askaniya Nova"*, **5**, 203–6.
———1956. (A contribution to a discussion.) Published in: *Problems of increasing milk and milk fat yield in dairy cattle.* Moscow.
KOKORINA, E. P. 1956a. The nature of the milk-ejection reflex in cows with different typological features in their higher nervous activity. Summary of Proceedings of a scientific conference of agricultural institutes on animal physiology. Leningrad.
———1956b. Features of the milk-ejection reflex in cows in which the mobility and equilibrium of cortical processes differs. *Dokl. Akad. Nauk SSSR*, **108**, 746–9.
———1958. Higher nervous activity and the milk yield of dairy cattle. *Zhurn. obshch. biologii*, **19**, 148–64.
———1959a. The procedure for catheterization of the udder. *Fiziol. zhurnal SSSR*, **45**, 1499–505.
———1959b. The conditioned reflex of milk ejection and its inhibition in cows with various typological peculiarities in their higher nervous activity. *Nauchn. soobshch. Inst. fiziol. im. I. P. Pavlova AN SSSR*, **1**, 191–3.
———1959c. Features of the milk-ejection reflex in cows in which the strength of the cortical nervous processes varies. *Tr. Inst. fiziol. im. I. P. Pavlova AN SSSR*, **8**, 46–50.
———1961. Agreement between secretory activity in separate quarters of the udder in cows. *Fiziol. zhurnal SSSR*, **47**, No. 1, 56–63.
KOROLEV, V. F. 1953. *Machine milking of cows.* Sel'khozgiz, Moscow.
KRESTINSKAYA, G. V. 1952. The receptors of the mammary gland. *Arkh. anat. gistol. i embriologii*, **29**, No. 4, 54.
KULIKOV, L. V. 1959. The processes of milk removal in cows. *Izv. Timiryaz. akad. s-kh. nauk*, **3**, 173–82.
KVASNITSKII, A. V., & KONYUKHOVA, V. A. 1954. *The application of Pavlov's teaching to animal husbandry.* Akad. Nauk UkrSSR, Kiev.
LEONTOVICH, A. V., MIRONOV, S., OLEANDROVA, A., & OSHE, E. 1932. Physiological materials relating to the principles of machine milking. *Elektr. sel'skogo khoz.*, No. 5–6, 48–63.
LEVITSKAYA, E. S. 1955. In vivo studies of the functioning of the discharge apparatus of the mammary gland in white mice. *Tr. Inst. fiziol. im. I. P. Pavlova*, **4**, 58–62.
LISKUN, E. F. 1912. German red cattle. *Tr. Byuro po zootekhniki*, 8.
LYAPUSTIN, A. K., & BULAK, A. N. 1952. Certain results from studies on increased yields and testing of a method for increasing the fat content

of the milk suggested by the milker K. M. Letsko. *Sov. zootekhniya,* No. 11, 37–41.
MARTYUGIN, D. D. 1944. Investigation of the act of suckling in calves. *Tr. Mosk. s.-kh. akad. im. K. A. Timiryazeva,* **31,** 149–84.
—— 1952. Machine milking of cows. *Sots. zhivotnovodstvo,* No. 4, 68–72.
—— 1954. The milk ejection process in cows in machine milking. *Zhivotnovodstvo,* No. 2, 56–8.
MAZHBITS, I. A. 1961. The use of posterior-pituitary extract in certain forms of lactational disorder in women in the post-natal period. *Akusherstvo i ginekologiya,* No. 1, 50–3.
NATOCHIN, YU. V. 1955. The effect of posterior-pituitary extract on the conditioned reflex activity of a dog. Summaries of 16th Conference of Students' Scientific Soc. of Novosibirsk State Med. Inst., p. 40.
NEMILOV, A. V. 1915. Some data on the histological structure of the mammary glands in Yaroslav cattle. *Tr. Byuro po zootekhniki,* No. 12, 3–19.
—— 1924. The connexion between the structure of the udder and the fine structure of the skin. *Izv. Gos. inst. opytn. agronomii,* **11,** Nos. 1–2, 27–9.
—— 1927. The biological foundations of the attributes of lactescence. *Tr. Otdela zootekhniki Gos. inst. opytn. agronomii,* **2,** 1–32.
NIKITIN, M. P. 1905. *The influence of the brain on the functioning of the mammary gland.* St. Pb.
NIKITIN, V. N. 1953. The biochemistry of lactation and the biosynthesis of milk fat. *Usp. sovr. biol.,* **35,** 55.
NIKITIN, V. N., TVERDUN, S. G., & DOKTOROVICH, N. L. 1953. Periodicity of the secretory process in the udder. *Zhurn. obshch. biologii,* **14,** 4, 275–89.
OGORODNII, YU. M. 1953. Changes in the composition of milk as an index of nervous regulation of the process of lactation and of its special features in cows of different yields. Conference on the physiology of farm animals, Summary of Proceedings, pp. 36–8.
OLENOV, YU. M. 1954. The reasons for differences in fat content in successively extracted portions of the milk. *Dokl. Akad. Nauk SSSR,* **97,** 361–4.
OLENOV, YU. M., & ZAKS, M. G. 1956. The role of conditioned reflex stimuli in the act of milk ejection in cows. *Dokl. Akad. Nauk SSSR,* **108,** 754–6.
OLENOV, YU. M., & NIUKKANEN, L. A. 1954. The effect of thermal stimuli on the removal and synthesis of milk fat. *Zhurn. obshch. biologii,* **15,** 414–27.
ORLOV, A. F. 1955. The receptory apparatus of the mammary gland and its physiological significance. Moscow Veterinary Academy, Summaries of Conference Proceedings on the physiology and pathology of farm animals, pp. 14–15.
PAVLOV, E. F., & MARKARYAN, A. KH. 1955. Liposecretory effects in the mammary gland when various cutaneous stimuli are employed. 2nd Conference on the physiology of farm animals, Summary of Proceedings, pp. 42–44. Moscow, Leningrad.
—— 1957. On the secretion of fat in the mammary gland. *Izv. Arm. Akad. nauk,* **10,** No. 1, 23–4.
PAVLOV, G. N. 1955a. Analysis of the milk-ejection reflex in goats using local cooling of the spinal cord. *Tr. Inst. fiziol. im. I. P. Pavlova AN SSSR,* **4,** 17–21.
—— 1955b. Methods for research on the nervous regulation of lactation. *Tr. Inst. fiziol. im. I. P. Pavlova,* **4,** 132–5.
PAVLOV, I. P. 1951. Further remarks on Dr. Mironov's work. *Pol. sob. soch.,* **1,** 588. Akad. Nauk SSSR.

POLIVODA, D. D. 1955. Higher nervous activity and milk secretion. Author's summary of thesis. Moscow.
POPOV, N. F. 1950. The nervous centres and their role in the regulation of tissue processes in the organism. *Izv. AN SSSR*, ser. biol., **6**, 124–36.
POPOVICH, D. 1958. The role of the hypothalamus in regulating the motor function of the mammary gland. *Dokl. Akad. Nauk SSSR*, **121**, 186–9.
PRITSKER, I. YA. 1941. Differences in the fat content of different portions of a milking in relation to various factors. *Dokl. VASKhNIL*, No. 7, 19–22.
PSHONIK, A. T. 1952. *The cerebral cortex and the receptor function of the organism.* Sov. nauka, Leningrad.
RIKHTER, I. D. 1939. *The biology of the mammary gland.* Sel'khozgiz.
SAVEL'YEV, A. S. 1947. The theory of milk ejection and the process of milking cows. *Vestn. zhivotnovodstva*, No. 3, 61–74.
——1949. The effect of vacuum on the state of the mammary glands in machine milking of cows. *Sots. tvarini*, **2**, 31–4.
SHAUMYAN, V. A. 1948. *Basic problems of the creation of breeds in dairy cattle.* Sel'khozgiz, Moscow.
——1955. Speech to the Technical Committee of the All-Union Ministry of Agriculture. *Zhivotnovodstvo*, No. 3, 124–6.
SHVABE, A. K. 1949. Effect of protein supply on the composition of milk. Collected papers of First All-Union Conference of Dairy Farm Workers. Moscow, 119–35.
——1951. Factors affecting variation in the protein content of milk. Papers of Second All-Union Conference on Dairying. Moscow, 164–9.
——1956. Variations in the content of the different constituents of the milk in the various fractions of a single milking. Summary of papers presented at a scientific conference of agricultural institutes on animal physiology. Leningrad.
SINESHCHEKOV, A. D. 1956a. Basic physiological features of the functioning of the mammary gland. In: *Problems of increasing milk yield and fat content in dairy cattle*, 6–33. Moscow.
——1956b. *The physiology of nutrition and the daily routine of farm animals.* Sel'khozgiz, Moscow.
SOLOV'YEV, A. A. 1952. *Increasing the fat content of cow's milk.* Sel'khozgiz, Moscow.
SOO, V. A. 1959. Changes in the elasticity of the mammary glands in women. *Akusherstvo i ginekologiya*, No. 5, 22–7.
SYUSYUKIN, A. A. 1955. Nervous regulation of milk removal in cows. Second Conference on the physiology of farm animals, Summary of Proceedings, pp. 57–60.
TROSHIN, I. P. 1936. The order in which the teats of the udder should be milked. *Sots. zhivotnovodstvo*, No. 11, 61–3.
TSAKHAEV, G. A. 1951. Reflex regulation of milk ejection. Author's summary of thesis. Leningrad.
——1953. Change in the secretory and motor function of the udder in goats under conditions of partial denervation. *Dokl. Akad. Nauk SSSR*, **93**, 1131–3.
——1959a. The secretory function of the mammary gland when the hypophysis is denervated. In: *Problems of the physiology of farm animals*, 3–19. Akad. Nauk Lit. SSR.
——1959b. The effect of excessively frequent milking on the quantity and composition of goat milk. Op. cit., 39–46.
TVERSKOI, G. B. 1953. The nature of the sensory impulses from the udder involved in reflex regulation of milk secretion. *Zhurn. obshch. biologii*, **14**, 349–59.
——1955a. The regulation of milk secretion. Second Conference on the physiology of farm animals, Summary of Proceedings, 66–73.

REFERENCES

———1955b. The sensitivity of the musculature of the ducts, cistern and teat sphincters of the cow's udder to the mediators of nervous stimuli and to posterior-pituitary extract. *Tr. Inst. fiziol. im. I. P. Pavlova AN SSSR*, **4**, 51–7.

———1959. The significance of innervation of the adenohypophysis in the regulation of milk secretion in goats. All-Union Meeting on the physiology and lactational biochemistry of farm animals, Summary of Proceedings, 281–4. Akad. Nauk SSSR.

———1960a. The effect of cervical sympathectomy and pituitary stalk section upon milk secretion in goats. *Dokl. Akad. Nauk SSSR*, **131**, 1215–18.

———1960b. Influence of cervical sympathectomy and pituitary stalk section upon milk secretion. *Nature*, **186**, 782–4.

TVERSKOI, G. B., & DYUSEMBIN, KH. 1955. The rate of milk secretion. *Tr. Inst. fiziol. im. I. P. Pavlova AN SSSR*, **4**, 75–80.

TYARKIN, S. S. 1953. An attempt at increasing the fat content of cow's milk by applying temperature stimuli to the udder. *Sots. zhivotnovodstvo*, No. 1, 74.

VAL'DMAN, V. A. 1958. Analysis of the milk-ejection reflex in unilateral deafferentation of the udder in goats. *Izv. AN Est. SSR*, **7**, No. 2, 106–13.

VLADIMIROVA, A. D. 1955. Reflex regulation of the blood circulation of the mammary gland. *Zhurn. obshch. biologii*, **16**, 141–55.

VOSKRESENSKII, L. N. 1916. Materials on the physiology of the mammary gland. *Tr. byuro po zootekhniki*, **14**, 3–52.

———1917. Materials on the physiology of milk removal. *Russk. fiziol. zhurn.*, **1**, Nos. 1–2, 102–4.

ZAKS, M. G. 1950. Problems of the neurohumoral regulation of lactation. *Usp. sovr. biol.*, **29**, 74–90.

———1951. New data on the functioning of the motor apparatus of the udder. *Collected papers of the Second All-Union Conference of Dairy Workers*, 160–3. Moscow.

———1955. Reflex regulation of the tone of the storage system of the udder and pressure within the udder. *Tr. Inst. fiziol. im. I. P. Pavlova AN SSSR*, **4**, 34–50.

———1956. Regulation of the removal of milk fat. *Usp. sovr. biol.*, **42**, 202–14.

ZAKS, M. G., EGOROVA, A. A., NIUKKANEN, L. A. & OLENOV, YU. M. 1952. Temperature effects on the udder as a means of increasing the fat content of milk. *Sov. zootekhniya*, No. 9, 14–22.

ZAKS, M. G., & OLENOV, YU. M. 1955. The mechanism of the removal of residual milk and fat distribution in it. 8th All-Union Congress of Physiologists, Pharmacologists and Biochemists, Summaries of Proceedings, 245–6. Kiev.

ZAKS, M. G., OLENOV, YU. M., & MAKEEVA, I. P. 1956. New data on the regulation of milk removal. *Zhurn. obshch. biologii*, **17**, 355–63.

ZAKS, M. G., OLENOV, YU. M., & SALTUP, B. N. 1954. The method of washing the udder with hot water before milking. *Zhivotnovodstvo*, No. 10, 104–7.

ZAKS, M. G., & PAVLOV, E. F. 1952. The correlation between udder capacity and the size of a single milking. *Tr. Soveshch. po biolog. osnovam povysh. produktivn. zhivotnovodstva*, 18–21. Moscow.

ZELIKOVSKAYA, Z. Z. 1953. The secretory process in the mammary gland. *Trudy L'vovsk. veter. in-ta*, **6**, 293–6.

ZOTIKOVA, I. N. 1955. The influence of the nervous system on the secretion and discharge of milk in white mice. *Tr. Inst. fiziol. im. I. P. Pavlova AN SSSR*, **4**, 63–7.

REFERENCES

ABRAHAMS, V. C., & PICKFORD, M. 1954. Simultaneous observations on the rate of urine flow and spontaneous uterine movements in the dog and their relationship to posterior lobe activity. *J. Physiol.*, **126**, 329–46.

ADAMS, H. P., & ALLEN, N. N. 1952. The value of oxytocin for reducing fluctuations in milk and fat yield. *J. Dairy Sci.*, **35**, 1117–20.

ANDERSSON, B. 1951a. Some observations on the neurohormonal regulation of milk ejection. *Acta physiol. scand.*, **23**, 1–7.

——1951b. The effect and localization of electrical stimulation of certain parts of the brain stem in sheep and goat. *Acta physiol. scand.*, **23**, 8–23.

——1951c. Further studies on the milk ejection mechanism in sheep and goats. *Acta physiol. scand.*, **23**, 24–30.

ANDERSSON, B., & MCCANN, S. M. 1955. Drinking, antidiuresis and milk ejection from electrical stimulation within the hypothalamus of the goat. *Acta physiol. scand.*, **35**, 191–202.

ANDREAS, A. 1954. *Mitt. dtsch. LandwGes.* 69, S. 1017–18. (Russian translation: Is twice-daily milking sufficient? *Se'skoe khoz. za rubezhom*, No. 3, 1955.)

ARMSBY, H. P. 1917. Nutrition of farm animals. N.Y.

BECK, G. H., FRYER, H. C., & ROARK, D. B. 1951. Use and interpretation of milk flow curves in measuring variations in the response of cows to machine milking. *J. Dairy Sci.*, **34**, 58–67.

BENSON, G. K., & FOLLEY, S. J. 1956. Oxytocin as stimulator for the release of prolactin from the anterior pituitary. *Nature, Lond.*, **177**, 700.

BÍLEK, J., & DOLEŽALEK, J. 1954. In: *Sborn. čsl. Akad. zeměd. Věd.*, **28**, A, 5, 423–49. (Russian translation: Study of thermal influences on the activity of the mammary gland. *Sel'skoe khoz. za rubezhom*, No. 3, 1955.)

BÍLEK, J., & JANOVSKY, M., 1955. Studium činnosti mléčne žlázi metodou skiaskopie. *Sborn. čsl. Akad. zeměd. Věd. (Živočišná Vyroba)*, **28**, 661–4.

CHRISTENSEN. I. C. 1949. Russian translation (1952) of: *Milking by machine.* 12th Int. Dairy Congr., **I**, sect. 1, 201–6.

COWIE, A. T., FOLLEY, S. J., CROSS, B. A., HARRIS, G. W., JACOBSOHN, DORA, & RICHARDSON, K. C. 1951. Terminology for use in lactational physiology. *Nature, Lond.*, **168**, 421.

CROSS, B. A. 1951. Suckling antidiuresis in rabbit. *J. Physiol.*, **114**, 447–53.

——1954. Milk ejection resulting from mechanical stimulation of mammary myoepithelium in the rabbit. *Nature, Lond.*, **173**, 450–1.

——1955a. The hypothalamus and the mechanism of sympathetico-adrenal inhibition of milk ejection. *J. Endoc.*, **12**, 15–28.

——1955b. Neurohormonal mechanism in emotional inhibition of milk ejection. *J. Endocrin.*, **12**, 29–37.

CROSS, B. A., & HARRIS, G. W., 1952. The role of the neurohypophysis in the milk-ejection reflex. *J. Endocrin.*, **8**, 148–61.

DENAMUR, R., et MARTINET, J. 1953. Sensibilité de la glande mammaire de la chèvre aux hormones posthypophysaires. *C.R. Soc. Biol., Paris*, **147**, 1217–20.

DONKER, J. D., KOSHI, J. H., & PETERSEN, W. E. 1954. The influence of oxytocin-induced udder evacuation on milk and butterfat production in a complete lactation. *J. Dairy Sci.*, **37**, 299–305.

DUERST, J. U. 1931. *Grundlagen der Rinderzucht.* Berlin.

ELLIOTT, G., & BRUMBY, P. J. 1955. Rate of milk secretion with increasing interval between milking. *Nature, Lond.*, **176**, 350–1.

ELY, F., & PETERSEN, W. E. 1941. Factors involved in the ejection of milk. *J. Dairy Sci.*, **24**, 211–23.

EMERSON, M. A. 1929. Some observations on the innervation of the udder and teats of the cow and their relations to milk production. *J. Amer. vet. med. Ass.*, **74**, 372–5. (Cited by Espe, 1946.)

ESPE, D. 1946. Russian translation (1950) of: *Secretion of milk*, Iowa State College Press, Ames, Iowa.

REFERENCES

FLUX, D. S., FOLLEY, S. J., & ROWLAND, S. J. 1954. The effect of adrenocorticotrophic hormone on the yield and composition of the milk of the cow. *J. Endocrin.*, **10**, 333–9.

FOLLEY, S. J. 1954. Recherches récentes sur la physiologie et la biochimie de la sécrétion lactée. Paris: Masson.

GAINES, W. L. 1951. A contribution to the physiology of lactation. *Amer. J. Physiol.*, **38**, 285.

GAINES, W. L., & SAANMANN, F. F. 1927. The quantity of milk present in the udder of the cow at milking time. *Amer. J. Physiol.*, **81**, 691–701.

GARRISON, E. R., & TURNER, C. W. 1936. The effect of udder irrigation and milking interval on milk secretion. Res. Bull. Mo. agric. exp. Sta. No. 234.

GAVIN, W. 1913. On the effects of administration of extracts of pituitary body and corpus luteum to milk cows. *Quart. Journ. exp. Physiol.*, **6**, 13.

GILDEMEISTER, M. 1914. Uber die sogenannte Härte tierischer Gewebe und ihre Messung. *Zeitschr. Biol.*, **63**, 183–200.

GOLTZ, F., und EWALD, I. R. 1896. Der Hund mit verkurtzten Rückenmark. *Pflüg. Arch. ges. Physiol.*, **63**, 362.

GOWEN, J. W., & TOBEY, E. R. 1928. Significance of the chemical composition of the secreting and dry mammary gland to milk secretion. *Journ. gen. Physiol.*, **12**, 123–8.

HAMMOND, J. 1936. The physiology of milk and butterfat secretion. *Vet. Rec.*, **16**, 519–35.

HARRIS, G. W. 1958. The central nervous system, neurohypophysis and milk ejection. *Proc. Roy. Soc.*, B. 149, 336–53

HARRIS. G. W., & JACOBSOHN, D. 1952. Functional grafts of the anterior pituitary gland. *Proc. roy. Soc., B*, **139**, 263–76.

HARRIS, G. W., & PICKLES, V. B. 1953. Reflex stimulation of the neurohypophysis and the nature of posterior-pituitary hormone(s). *Nature, Lond.*, **172**, 1049.

HEIDENHAIN, R. 1886. *A manual of physiology*, **5**, Pt. 1. The physiology of excretory processes. (Translated from German.) Gl. voenn. medits. upr. St. Pb.

HERODOTUS. History. In 9 books. Books 1 and 2, translated by F. T. Mishchenko, 1888.

IRVING, G. W. 1944. *The chemistry and physiology of hormones.* American Association for Advancement of Science: Lancaster, Pa., 28–46.

JACOBSOHN, D. 1949. The effect of transection of the hypophyseal stalk on the mammary gland of lactating rabbit. *Acta physiol. scand.*, **19**, fasc. 1, 10–18.

JENSEN, M. T. 1949. Russian translation (1952) of: The correct method of milking by hand and its importance. A training method in the right milking technique. 12th Int. Dairy Congr., **I**, sect. 1, 190–200.

KALLIALA, H., & KARVONEN, M. J. 1951. Antidiuresis during suckling in lactating women. *Ann. Med. exper. Fenn.*, **29**, 233.

KALLIALA, H. M., KARVONEN, M. J., & LEPPÄNEN, V. 1952. Release of antidiuretic hormone during nursing in dog. *Ann. Med. exper. Fenn.*, **30**, 96.

KIRCHNER, M. 1907. *Handbuch der Milchwirtschaft.* Berlin.

KLEIBER, M. 1954. Precursor product relationship for milk formation in the intact dairy cow. *Rev. canad. Biol.*, **13**, 333–50.

KNODT, C. B., & PETERSEN, W. E. 1944. The effect of complete evacuation of mammary gland by Pitocin upon milk and fat production. *J. Dairy Sci.*, **27**, 449–457.

KOSHI, J. H., & PETERSEN, W. E. 1955. Complementary milk and its relation to lactation. *J. Dairy Sci.*, **38**, 788–96.

KRZYWANEK, FR. W., & BRÜGGEMANN, H. 1931. Zum Studium der Milchsekretion. II. Mitt. Der Druckablauf in allen 4 Zitzen des Euters während des Milchentzuges. *Milchw. Forsch.*, **11**, 371–8.

REFERENCES

LINZELL, J. E. 1950. Vasomotor nerve fibres to the mammary glands of the cat and dog. *Quart. J. exper. Physiol.*, **35**, 424–9.
——1952. The silver staining of myoepithelial cells particularly in the mammary gland, and their relation to the ejection of milk. *J. Anat., Lond.*, **86**, 49–57.
——1954. Some observations on the use of the perfused lactating mammary gland. *Rev. canad. Biol.*, **13**, 291–8.
——1955. Some observations on the contractile tissue of the mammary gland. *J. Physiol.*, **130**, 257–67.
MCMEEKAN, C. T., & BRUMBY, P. J. 1956. Milk production and interval between milking. *Nature, Lond.*, **178**, 799.
MOSIMANN, W. 1949. Zur Anatomie der Rindermilchdrüse und über die Morphologie ihrer segmentierenden Teile. *Acta anat.*, **8**, 347–78.
NICKERSON, K. BONSES, R. W., DOUGLAS, G., CONDLIFFE, P., & VIGNEAUD V. DU., 1954. Oxytocin and milk ejection. *Amer. J. Obstet. Gynec.*, **67**, 1028.
NOBLE, R. L. 1954. The nervous and hormonal control of lactation. *Rev. canad. Biol.*, **13**, 351–8.
OTT, J., & SCOTT, J. C. 1910. The action of infundibulin upon the mammary secretion. *Proc. Soc. exper. Biol., N.Y.*, **8**, 48–9.
PAGE, E. W. 1946. The value of plasma pitocin determination in obstetrics. *Amer. J. Obstet. Gynec.*, **52**, 1014.
PEETERS, G., & COUSSENS, R. 1950. The influence of the milking act on the diuresis of the lactating cow. *Arch. int. Pharmacodyn.*, **84**, 209–20.
PEETERS, G., COUSSENS, R., & SIERENS, G. 1949. Physiology of the nerves in bovine mammary gland. *Arch. int. Pharmacodyn.*, **79**, 75–82.
PEETERS, G., & MASSERT, L. 1947. *Arch. int. Pharmacodyn.*, **74**, 83. (Cit. W. G. Whittlestone, 1951.)
PERRIN, D. R. 1954. The composition of cow's milk during the course of lactation. *J. Dairy Res.*, **21**, 55–62.
PETERSEN, W. E. 1944. The action of the mechanical milker in relation to completeness of milking and udder injury. *J. Dairy Sci.*, **27**, 433–40.
——1950. Dairy science, its principles and practice. Chicago-Philadelphia —N.Y.
PETERSEN, W. E., & LUDVICK, L. M. 1942. The hormonal nature of the factor causing the let down of milk. *Fed. Proc.*, **1**, 66.
PETERSEN, W. E., PALMER, L. S., & ECKLES, C. H. 1929. The synthesis and secretion of milk fat. *Amer. J. Physiol.*, **90**, 573–99.
PETERSEN, W. E., & RIGOR, F. W. 1932. Relation of pressure to rate and quality of milk secretion. *Proc. Soc. exper. Biol., N.Y.*, **30**, 254–64.
PICKLES, V. R. 1953. Blood flow estimations as indices of mammary activity. *J. Obstet. Gynaec., Brit. Emp.*, **60**, 301.
——1954. Variation in the rate of blood flow in human mammary gland. *Rev. canad. Biol.*, **13**, 299–306.
POJARVI, J. 1954. Beiträge zur Wirkung der Dauer der Melpause auf die Intänsitet der Milchsecretion des Kuheuters. *Maatalouss. Aikakausk.*, **26**, 50.
PROKS, J. 1928. De l'individualité des glandes mammaires chez les vaches. *Lait*, **8**, 553–62.
RAGSDALE, A. C., BRODY, S., & TURNER, C. W. 1921. The variation in the percentage of fat in successive portions of cow's milk. *J. Dairy Sci.*, **4**, 448–50.
——1924. The rate of milk secretion as affected by an accumulation of milk in the mammary gland. *J. Dairy Sci.*, **7**, 249.
REISET, J. 1849. Expériences sur la composition du lait dans certaines phases de la traite, et sur les avantages de la traite fractionnée pour la fabrication du beurre. *Ann. Chim. (Phys.)*, III-e sér., **25**, 82–92.

REFERENCES

RICHARDSON, K. C. 1949. Contractile tissues in the mammary gland with the special reference to myoepithelium in the goat. *Proc. roy. Soc.*, B., **136**, 30–45.

RÖBEN, K. 1954. *Mitt. dtsch. LandwGes.*, Bd. 69, H. 48, 1. 1140–2. (Russian translation: Basic rules for machine milking of cows. *Sel'skoe khoz. za rubezhom*, No. 3, 1955.)

ROSS, H. E., & WINTER, H. 1934. Study of the effect of removing foremilk on the fat content of remainder of the milking. *Bull. Cornell agric. Exp. Sta.*, No. 589.

SCHÄFER, E. A. 1913. On the effect of pituitary and corpus luteum extracts on the mammary gland in the human subject. *Quart. J. exper. Physiol.*, **6**, 17.

SCHMIDT-MÜLHEIM, 1883. Beiträge zur Kenntnis der Milchsecretion. *Pflüg. Arch. ges. Physiol.*, **30**, 602–20.

SMITH, W. R., & PETERSEN, W. E. 1948. The effect of preparation of the cow on the rate of milking. *J. Dairy Sci.*, **31**, 589.

SPRAIN, D. P., SMITH, W. R., TYLER, W. J., & FOSGATE, O. P. 1954. The effect on milk and fat production of injection of Pitocin. *J. Dairy Sci.*, **37**, 195–201.

SPRINGER, R. 1914. Untersuchungen über die Resistenz (die sogenannte Härte) menschlicher Muskeln. *Zeitschr. Biol.*, **63**, 201–22.

SWETT, W. W., & MATTHEWS, C. A. 1953. The inside of a cow. *Certif. Milk*, 8–9.

TURNER, C. W. 1933. *The physiology and biochemistry of milk secretion.* Dairy Husbandry Dpt. of Mo. (Cited by Espe, 1946.)

——1934. The functional individuality of the mammary gland of the dairy cow. Res. Bull. Mo. agric. exp. Sta., 211.

——1935. The secretion of milk and milking process. Res. Bull. Mo. agric. exp. Sta., 346.

TURNER, H. G. 1953. Dependence of residual milk in the udder of the cow upon total yield. Its bearing upon supposed inhibition of secretion. *Aust. J. agric. Res.*, **4**, 118.

——1955a. Changes in capacity of the udder of dairy cow during the course of lactation. *Aust. J. agric. Res.*, **6**, 145–60.

——1955b. Sources of variation in residual milk and fat in dairy cows. *Aust. J. agric. Res.*, **6**, 514–29.

——1955c. The effect of inequal intervals between milkings upon the milk production and diurnal variations in milk secretion. *Aust. J. agric. Res.*, **6**, 530–8.

TVERSKOI, G. B. 1960b. Influence of cervical sympathectomy and pituitary stalk section upon milk secretion. *Nature, Lond.*, **186**, 782–4.

VERNEY, E. B. 1947. The antidiuretic hormone and the factors which determine its release. *Proc. roy. Soc.*, B., **135**, 25–106.

VIGNEAUD, V. DU, RESSLER, CH., SWAN, J. M., ROBERTS, C. W., KATSOJANNIS, P. G., & GORDON, S. 1953a. The synthesis of an octopeptide amide with the hormonal activity of oxytocin. *Amer. chem. Soc.*, **75**, 7879–80.

VIGNEAUD, V. DU, RESSLER, CH., & TRIPPET, ST. 1953b. The sequence of aminoacids in oxytocin, with a proposal for structure of oxytocin. *J. biol. Chem.*, **205**, 949–57.

WHITTLESTONE, W. G. 1950. Some recent experiments on the problem of milk ejection. *Proc. N.Z. Soc. Anim. Prod.*, **10**, 67–80.

——1951. Studies of milk ejection in the dairy cow. *N.Z. J. Sci. Tech.*, A., **32**, 1–20.

——1952. The milk ejection activity of extracts of the posterior-pituitary gland. *J. Endocrin.*, **8**, 89–95.

——1953a. The milk ejection response of the sow to standard doses of oxytocic hormone. *J. Dairy Res.*, **20**, 13–15.

———1953b. Variations in the fat content of milk throughout the milking process. *J. Dairy Res.*, **20**, 146–53.
———1954a. Managing the milking machine. *N.Z.J. Agric.*, **87**, 218–22.
———1954b. The physical property of cow's milk as influenced by stage of lactation. *J. Dairy Res.*, **21**, 50–4.
———1954c. Intramammary pressure changes in the lactating sow. *J. Dairy Res.*, **21**, 183–7.
———1954d. The effect of adrenaline on the milk ejection response of the sow. *J. Endocrin.*, **10**, 167–72.
WHITTLESTONE, W. G., & PERRIN, D. R. 1954. Variation of the fat content of human milk during suckling. *J. Dairy Res.*, **21**, 204–6.
WHITTLESTONE, W. G., PERRIN, D. R., PARKINSON, R. D., & TURNER, C. W. 1952. Frequency of discharge of pituitary milk "let down" hormone. *J. Dairy Sci.*, **35**, 894–8.
WHITTLESTONE, W. G., & PHILLIPS, D. S. 1951. Automatic apparatus for drawing the milk ejection curves of dairy cows under controlled milking conditions. *J. Dairy Res.*, **20**, 319–26.
WOODWARD, T. E., HOTIS, R. P., & GRAVES, R. R. 1936. Incomplete milking in relation to milk production. *Tech. Bull. U.S. Dep. Agric.*, No. 522.
ZEITZSCHMANN, O. 1923. Über die Milchsecretion und Milchströmung bei der Kuh. *Dtsch. tierärztl. Wschr.*, No. 10, 109–11.

SUBJECT INDEX

acetylcholine
   effect on musculature of ducts, 50
adrenaline
   oxytocin antagonist, 48-9, 81-2
alveolar milk, 9-21
   rate of flow to cistern, 14
   retention, 15-21
antidiuretic hormone
   milk ejection, 45-6

breeding
   important udder characteristics, 156

capacity function
   definitions, 8
   variation in course of lactation, 24-5
   variation with lactation number, 25
casein
   fractions of a milking, 138-40
cistern, *see also* intracisternal pressure
   milk secretion, 136-8
   tone of musculature, 22
cisternal milk, 9-21
citrate
   fractions of a milking, 139

digestion
   linked with lactation, 37, 65, 97

excretion
   kidney function and lactation, 46-7

higher nervous activity
   Pavlovian classification, 103
   types of cow, 103-4
hypothalamus
   milk ejection, 37-9

intracisternal pressure, *see also* milk secretion
   critical value, 25-6
   discussion, 21-6
   measurement, 31-3
   variation during milking, 66-70
intramammary pressure, *see also* milk secretion
   woman, 174-7

liposecretory reflexes, 122-4

mammary gland
   induration in woman, 176
   vital microscopy in mice, 33, 49, 124
milk
   reabsorption of constituents, 9
milk discharge, 18-21, 69
milk ejection
   beginning, 29
   definition, 4, 27
   discussion, 27-110
   duration of effect, 57-60
   hormonal link, 40, 43-51
   inhibition, 78-83, 101-2
   latent period, 56, 60, 102
   methods of study, 28-34
   reflex arc, 34-43
   sows, 99
   theories reviewed, 104-10
   two-stage act, 65-83
milk ejection stimuli
   conditioned, 19-20, 86-104
   differentiation, 64
   mechanical, 55-7
   sexual, 64-5
   thermal, 62-4, 74
   vagus, 65
milk fat
   effect of complete milking, 141-9
   effect of frequent milking, 149-52
   fractions of a milking, 114-27, 140
   general discussion, 133-8
   location of reserve, 121-7
   quality variations, 130-3
   secretory variations in different parts of parenchyma, 127-33
   successive milkings, 111-4
milk secretion
   definition, 105-6
   effect of milking, 142-52

efferent innervation, 124
independent of milk ejection, 36
intramammary pressure, 4, 6, 22, 31, 143, 154–6
milk synthesis
efffect of milking, 124
milking
blood flow increased, 124
by hand, 166–8
by machine, 168–73
complete, effect on milk secretion, 141–9
compression frequency, 56–7
continuous recording, 29
frequency, 24, 57–61, 149–60
palm *versus* fingers, 64
pessimum, 88
posthumous, 134–5
preparation of cow, 160–3
stages, 28
stimulation of receptors, 55
successive quarters, 53
udder massage, 162–6
myoepithelium
efferent innervation, 40–3
oxytocin, 50
reflex control, 17–23
short arc, 41

oxytocin
destruction in blood, 48
effects in women, 177
exogenous, effect on neurohypophysial secretion, 145
milk ejection, 39, 45–51

parasympathetic innervation
absence from udder, 40–1
pituitary, posterior
milk-ejection hormone, 43–51
pituitary stalk section
milk ejection, 39–40

reflex arc
afferent fibres, 34–37
efferent fibres, 40

summary, 41–3
reflex stimuli
conditioned, 86–104
mechanical, 83–6
neural, 71
neurohumoral, 72
thermal, 147–50
unconditioned, 86–104
residual milk
stimulates secretion, 151
total removal, 8

storage system
description, 1–3
exteroceptive stimuli, 19–20
interoceptive stimuli, 17–19
radiographic study, 33–4
tone, 18, 21
strippings
definition, 10
procedure, 75–6
suckling
calves and goats, 53, 69
conditioned reflex, 98
mechanical stimulus, 86
thermal stimulus, 62
various animals, 1–2
supraoptic nuclei
milk ejection, 37–9
sympathetic nerves
motor apparatus, 40

teat
reflexogenic zone, 54
sphincter, 86
teat sphincters
variations in tone, 172

udder
dynamics of filling, 8–21
effect of denervation, 17–18
massage, 162–6
sensitivity zones, 54–5

vasopressin
milk ejection, 45–6